THE PSYCHIATRIC PROFESSIONS
Power, Conflict, and Adaptation in a Psychiatric Hospital Staff

THE UNIVERSITY OF NORTH
CAROLINA PRESS · CHAPEL HILL

THE
PSYCHIATRIC
PROFESSIONS

Power, Conflict, and Adaptation
in a Psychiatric Hospital Staff

WILLIAM A. RUSHING

This book is dedicated to my wife
Kay

PREFACE

During the past decade the problem of mental health has received increased attention from sociologists. Much of this attention has been devoted to the study of societal and community factors which precipitate, or at least are correlated with, mental illness. Relatively less attention has been devoted to the study of persons who treat mental patients. Yet from a practical as well as a sociological standpoint, the study of mental health professions is equally important. Effective modern psychiatric treatment in mental hospitals consists of the application and co-ordination of the activities of professional persons with diverse therapeutic skills, which is a matter of social structure and social organization. And the study of social structure and social organization is central to the sociologist's interest. This book reports on problems which members of the recreation, social work, clinical psychology, and psychiatric nursing professions may face as members of a modern mental hospital—in the present case, the department of psychiatry of a university school of medicine. The ambitious educational, therapeutic, and research objectives of this hospital suggest that it is an ideal place for persons who are devoted to applying their talents to the problem of mental illness. Indeed, it is ideal—in many respects. In some respects, however, it is not; characteristics of the hospital social structure pose problems for and create tensions among hospital staff members. These are the concern of this book.

Research for this book began in the Spring of 1959 and was completed in the Summer of 1960 while I was a graduate student in the Department of Sociology and Anthropology, The University of North Carolina at Chapel Hill. During this period

I was also a member of the Social Research Section, Division of Health Affairs, under the direction of Professor Harvey L. Smith. Affiliation with this program facilitated my access to the hospital and its personnel. I was able to observe numerous ward rounds, "team" meetings, diagnostic conferences, and other conferences and meetings, as well as the work activities of various hospital personnel. My role in most cases was that of observer, which enabled me to make many of the observations reported in this book. I also conducted a number of interviews. Although interviews were scheduled to last for one hour, a number ran considerably longer. Several lasted over two hours, and three took over two and one-half hours.

The research progressed through four overlapping stages. First, an intensive study was made of the recreation service, followed by a study of social workers. For recreation, analysis focused on the problems of social influence, role-making, and the processes involved in the development of social norms. The phenomenon of social influence received additional attention in the study of social workers. For both services, data revealed that the problem of social influence differs depending upon whether the actor attempts to influence others' overt instrumental acts or their attitudes toward him. Study of clinical psychologists substantiated many of the observations of the first two studies and revealed more explicitly certain social-psychological functions of social norms. Finally, the study of psychiatric nurses focused on the problems of nurses' influencing doctors to change treatment orders which they considered detrimental to the patients' welfare.

All groups were studied within a common theoretical framework, which is essentially a social-psychological one. Consequently, the framework, as well as specific questions asked, often deviated from those of other field studies in social organizations. Rather than concentrating on the "functioning of the social system," attention was directed to what might be called the social psychology of social structure, to such problems as: the effect of social structure on the individual's role performance, the "conditioning" effect of the normative order on his attempts to influence the behavior and attitudes of others, and the functions of social norms and the processes of their development.

Thus, although the study of hospital social organization and tensions among mental health professions may be of practical importance, I am not concerned with these problems alone. I am concerned with a search for greater understanding of social behavior and certain dynamics of social structure in general. Indeed, it is hoped that the detailed sociological analysis of concrete problems faced by members of a modern mental hospital will contribute in some small measure to the sociological understanding of social behavior in general—not just hospital social behavior. This book, therefore, has two objectives: (1) To contribute to academic sociology through the empirical study of the psychiatric professions. (I would be dishonest if I said this were not the major objective.) (2) To highlight for non-sociologists, particularly those persons who work in mental hospitals, the contributions sociology may make toward understanding important human events in mental hospitals. I hope, too, that hospital administrators and members of the medical profession, who so much control what occurs in mental hospitals, will derive some practical benefit from this book; I would especially hope that the findings of this book will have some influence on their decisions affecting psychiatry's so-called "ancillary" professions. And, in particular, I hope that members of these "ancillary" professions and psychiatric nursing will achieve understanding of certain problems they encounter and endure as members of a modern mental hospital.

I want to acknowledge my debt to several persons and agencies. I am especially indebted to Professor Harvey L. Smith, who directed the research, for his counsel and suggestions throughout the course of the study. To Professor John W. Thibaut, I owe a strong intellectual debt for certain ideas appearing in the book. Those sections dealing with the functions and development of social norms especially bear his influence. I want to thank Professors Lee J. Axelson and James A. Geschwender for their critical comments on the first two chapters. I want also to thank my wife, Kay, for typing the entire manuscript, as well as for her editorial assistance. I am indebted to the National Institute of Mental Health and the Institute for Research in Social Science, The University of North Carolina at Chapel Hill, for financial support during the course of the research, and to the University of Wisconsin for a financial grant which aided in the final stages of writing the manuscript. I should also like to thank the Ford Foundation for a grant extended through its program for assisting American university presses in the publication of works in the humanities and the social sciences.

And to those members of the psychiatric professions who voluntarily gave of their time and made this book possible, I am deeply appreciative.

William A. Rushing
Madison, Wisconsin

TABLE OF CONTENTS

xi

PART I

INTRODUCTION

1 INTRODUCTION

The past few years have witnessed several studies demonstrating the usefulness of sociological analysis for understanding social behavior in mental hospitals.[1] These studies have often shown, contrary to the viewpoint of the psychiatrically oriented, that behavior is often better explained in terms of the hospital social *milieu* than it is by reference to personality factors. This book is also concerned with the effect of the hospital *milieu* on social behavior. Specifically, it investigates how professional persons attempt to cope with certain problems they face as members of a mental hospital, problems such as too little prestige and "professional respect," poorly defined roles, and disagreements between themselves and others regarding their proper duties. The persons studied include members of psychiatric nursing and three of psychiatry's so-called "ancillary" professions—recreation, clinical psychology, and social work. The major focus is on the relationships between members of these professions and psychiatrists. The setting for the study is the Department of Psychiatry in a university teaching hospital.

1. For some examples, see: Ivan Belknap, *Human Problems of a State Mental Hospital* (New York: McGraw-Hill Book Company, 1956); William A. Caudill, *The Psychiatric Hospital as a Small Society* (Cambridge: Harvard University Press, 1958); H. Warren Dunham and S. K. Weinberg, *The Culture of the State Mental Hospital* (Detroit: Wayne State University Press, 1960); Erving Goffman, *Asylums* (New York: Doubleday and Company, Inc., 1961); and Alfred H. Stanton and Morris S. Schwartz, *The Mental Hospital* (New York: Basic Books, Inc., 1954). For a review and evaluation of a number of studies of mental hospitals, see Amitai Etzioni, "Interpersonal and Structural Factors in the Study of Mental Hospitals," *Psychiatry*, XXIII (1960), 13-22.

Much of the sociological research in mental hospitals has, directly or indirectly, been concerned with patients and the effect of the hospital *milieu* on patient welfare.[2] This issue receives no concern in this book, which is based on the premise that the study of mental health professions is worthwhile in and of itself, regardless of any implication the findings may have for patient care. This is not to say that the social processes described in this book are unrelated to patient welfare; we are sure that there is a relationship. However, we are not concerned with this. Concern is exclusively with the mental health professions, not their patients.

A basic theme pervading the pages of this book is that an adequate understanding of modern mental hospitals, particularly the problems of professional persons who work in them, requires a comprehension of the concepts of institution, institutionalization process, and social role. Since these concepts are so important, it will be wise at this time to introduce the reader to our definitions of them.

Institutions refer to rules (norms) which define the conduct of persons who are in continuous interaction so that both know what to expect of each other, and both feel that each should conform to these agreed upon expectations.[3] At one time in American society, for example, relationships between husbands and wives were strongly regulated by rules which clearly defined the wife as the subordinate and her duties exclusively as housekeeping and caring for children; the husband, defined as the superior, made most of the important decisions and provided for the family's economic welfare. These rules were generally accepted by most adult members of rural America, so that marriage partners knew what to expect of each other. Male and female "definitions of the situation" were congruent, and the husband-wife relationship was highly institutionalized. Today, there is less agreement on the rules of marriage relationships. Married females frequently engage in occupational pursuits and sometimes demand a position

2. See in particular, Alfred H. Stanton and Morris S. Schwartz, "Observations on Dissociation as Social Participation," *Psychiatry*, XII (1949), 339-54.
3. For a concise statement of institutions in this sense, see A. R. Radcliff-Brown, "Introduction," in *Social Structure and Function in Primitive Society* (Glencoe: The Free Press, 1952), p. 9. For a general discussion of the concept of institution in sociology, see Howard B. Kaplan, "The Concept of Institution: A Review, Evaluation, and Suggested Research Procedure," *Social Forces*, XXXIX (1960), 176-80.

equal rather than subordinate to their husbands. Consequently, definitions of the situation may not be congruent, with marriage partners often having unclear and conflicting expectations of each other. The absence of agreed upon rules in social relationships is often accompanied by tension, which in marriage relationships is partially reflected by the increased divorce rate. Tension may be reduced, however, when individuals come to a consensus regarding their expectations of each other. The process of arriving at consensus is called the institutionalization process.

When different rules apply to different members of a group, a division of labor exists and we speak of social roles. For example, there is a division of labor between husband and wife; each performs different functions which assure the survival of the group, so that we speak of the role of the husband and the role of the wife. When rules do not clearly define and differentiate between group members' duties, the group and its relationships are not fully institutionalized, but may be in the process of becoming so. As noted above, this may be accompanied by conflict and tension among group members. (More attention will be given later in this chapter to the concept of social role, where its use and limitations in this study are spelled out in detail. For the moment, the above statement will suffice.)

The same reasoning may be applied to complex social organizations, such as mental hospitals. These organizations involve a division of labor so that there is a complex of interrelated social roles. In some cases, role relationships are highly institutionalized; in other cases, as we shall see in this book, they may be poorly institutionalized—members may disagree regarding the division of duties among them. The modern treatment-oriented mental hospital, characterized by a complex division of labor consisting of highly skilled professional groups, is an organization currently undergoing institutionalization. A prerequisite for an institutionalized structure of social relationships is the mutual agreement among individuals regarding their expectations—that is, common definitions of their respective roles. There are indications that such clear-cut mutual role definitions frequently do not exist in mental hospitals.[4]

4. See Harvey L. Smith and Daniel J. Levinson, "The Major Aims and Organizational Characteristics of Hospitals," in Milton Greenblatt, Daniel J. Levinson, and Richard H. Williams (eds.), *The Patient and the Mental Hospital* (Glencoe: The Free Press, 1957), p. 5; and Harvey L. Smith, "Professional Strains and the Hospital Context," *ibid.*, pp. 9-13.

For instance, the oldest of the mental health professions—psychiatry, clinical psychology, and psychiatric social work—have yet to arrive at a public, institutionalized agreement on the question of who is qualified to conduct psychotherapy.[5] One investigation of this trio reveals that the conceptions of psychiatrists and psychologists are inconsistent regarding the latter's functions. Most psychiatrists view psychologists exclusively as persons who administer routine psychological tests, whereas psychologists tend to view themselves as knowledgeable and skillful in the areas of psychological theory and research. While this investigation indicates reasonable agreement between social workers and psychiatrists regarding the former's skills, there is wide disagreement regarding the social workers' interviewing skills.[6] Studies of the individual professions also support the view that mental hospitals are in the process of institutionalization. A study of the profession of psychiatry concludes that its relationships with the medical profession, as well as with its "ancillary" professions, social science, and the public, are not clearly and firmly established.[7] Wilensky and Lebeaux, in their analysis of "the emergence of a social work profession," [8] describe social workers (including psychiatric social workers) as oscillating between a psychological and a sociological focus in their casework role. On the one hand, concern is with intrapsychic conflict and "helping an individual to identify, clarify, and understand his own difficulties" so that the distinction from psychotherapy is not sharp.[9] On the other hand, social work has a history of "sociological" emphasis; attention is directed to the community social structure which created the "case," and to "environment manipulation" (vocational rehabilitation, welfare services, etc.). The social worker, although leaning toward the former role, still has not clarified, to himself or to others, the exact definition of his role. There are indications also that the social worker's role in medical schools is not well established. A committee of the National Association of Social

5. See especially Harvey L. Smith, "The Value Context of Psychology," *American Psychologist,* IX (1954), 101-5.
6. Alvin Zander, Arthur R. Cohen, and Ezra Stotland, *Role Relations in the Mental Health Professions* (Ann Arbor: Institute for Social Research, 1957), pp. 42 and 65.
7. Harvey L. Smith, "Psychiatry: A Social Institution in Process," *Social Forces,* XXXIII (1955), 337-46.
8. Harold L. Wilensky and Charles N. Lebeaux, *Industrial Society and Social Welfare* (New York: Russell Sage Foundation, 1958).
9. *Ibid.,* p. 290.

Workers, which studied the problem of social workers' participation in medical school education, concludes: "Social workers are not clear about what they have to offer, nor is the medical profession apparently clear about what they want." [10] The profession of clinical psychology, less than fifty years old and deriving from an academic background, has yet to establish a clear-cut image as a practicing profession. As the authors of one study remark: "The role of the clinical psychologist is in the stage of 'becoming' and expanding." [11] The academic tradition of clinical psychology and the academic training clinical psychologists receive[12] are likely to pose special problems for psychologists who are defined as "ancillary" and, therefore, subordinate to members of another profession who are their status equals in a university setting.[13]

Research on the other mental health professions is also suggestive. Studies reveal that the psychiatric nurse, trained in traditional nursing skills, does not clearly know what is expected of her in a psychiatric setting,[14] nor how to perform psychotherapeutic duties once they have been assigned to her.[15] Other research points to an inconsistency among nurses regarding their appropriate role in mental hospitals.[16] Finally, one set of studies of psychiatrists, nurses, and attendants, concludes that among

10. Report of "The Medical and Psychiatric Social Work Sections of the Joint Committee on Participation in Medical Education," National Association of Social Workers, Chicago, 1960, p. 1. (Mimeographed.)
11. Zander, Cohen, and Stotland, *Role Relations in the Mental Health Professions*, p. 5.
12. Edgar F. Borgatta, "The Certification of Academic Professions: The Case of Psychology," *American Sociological Review*, XXIII (1958), 302-6.
13. Smith and Levinson, "The Major Aims and Organizational Characteristics of Mental Hospitals," p. 7.
14. William A. Caudill, *et al.*, "Social Structure and Interaction Process on a Psychiatric Ward," *American Journal of Orthopsychiatry*, XX (1952), 322; and G. E. Tudor, "A Sociopsychiatric Nursing Approach to Intervention in a Problem of Mutual Withdrawal in a Hospital Ward," *Psychiatry*, XV (1952), 193-217.
15. Charlotte G. Schwartz, "Problems for Psychiatric Nurses in Playing a New Role on a Mental Hospital Ward," in Greenblatt, Levinson, and Williams, *The Patient and the Mental Hospital*, pp. 402-6.
16. Harry W. Martin and Ida Harper Simpson, *Patterns of Psychiatric Nursing: A Survey of Psychiatric Nursing in North Carolina* (Chapel Hill: Institute for Research in Social Science, 1956); and Dorothea Scott, "The Relation of the Uniform to the Professional Self-Image of the Psychiatric Nurse," (unpublished Master's thesis, Department of Sociology and Anthropology, University of North Carolina, 1960).

these groups there is "wide variation in individual role performance within a given (hospital) setting—greater variation, perhaps, than is envisaged in many sociological theories." [17]

These studies, pointing as they do to a lack of clarity in role
definitions among mental health professions, suggest that mental
hospitals have not yet attained a high level of internal institutionalization.

Problems of institutionalization may be further complicated
if administrators take a negative view of formal, rigid rules and
the use of authority. There is evidence that psychiatrists frequently do this.[18] In the hospital under study, for example, there
is no organizational chart indicating who has authority over
whom. Also, psychiatrists have even refused to specify the duties
they expect from an "ancillary" service (social work). They argued that since duties vary with individual personalities, formal
statements regarding respective role duties are useless; instead,
such problems should be worked out on a "one-to-one" basis with
the persons with whom one works.[19]

On the basis of the foregoing, we would expect many points
of tension among hospital personnel. Nevertheless, psychiatric
administrators frequently expressed little need to resolve conflict
among personnel because, they claimed, such conflicts rarely
arose. To the extent that they do, one believes that "good competent and mature people can work these problems out"; consequently, administrative action is rarely needed. The Department
is viewed by at least one psychiatrist as "an autonomous business
—everything runs itself with a minimum of intervention." The
psychiatrists' disclaimers notwithstanding, early field contact with

17. G. M. Carstairs, *et al.,* "Ideology, Personality, and Role Definition:
Studies of Hospital Personnel," in Greenblatt, Levinson, and Williams,
The Patient and the Mental Hospital, p. 229.
18. See Robert N. Rapoport and Rhona Sofer Rapoport, " 'Democratization'
and 'Authority' in a Therapeutic Community," *Behavioral Science,* II
(1957), 128-33. Some argue that "bureaucracy," in the form of hierarchies
of authority and prestige and formal and rigid rules, creates dissatisfaction
and stress among the "ancillary" staff and should be abolished. On this
point, see Milton Greenblatt, Richard H. York and Ester Lucile Brown,
From Custodial to Therapeutic Patient Care in Mental Hospitals (New
York: Russell Sage Foundation, 1955), pp. 421-22. See also Mark Lefton,
Simon Dinitz and Benjamin Pasamanick, "Decision-Making in a Mental
Hospital: Real, Perceived, and Ideal," *American Sociological Review,*
XXIV (1959), 822-29.
19. See pp. 61-63 below.

the Department confirmed our expectation of conflict among departmental members. As examples, psychiatrists and social workers clearly disagreed on the latter's role duties, as well as what the duties of psychiatric residents should be; the psychologists' preference for research and teaching activities was not consistent with the psychiatrists' demands for diagnostic services; the nurse-resident relationship was threatened by a role contradiction, with the subordinate nurse often knowing more about psychiatric care than the neophyte resident physician; psychiatrists and nurses appeared to have ambiguous expectations of the recreation service, as well as not sharing the latter's conception of recreation's function in the Department.

It should be noted that institutions may apply to attitudes as well as to overt behavior. Although individuals may agree on their role duties so that few differences in definitions of situations exist, and the problems of co-ordinating overt role performances are minimal, role performers may have little respect and appreciation for each other. To the extent that such sentiments are important, and they usually are, dissatisfaction results. For example, members of the "ancillary" professions frequently complained of the lack of "professional respect" psychiatrists expressed toward them and their work; they complained that psychiatrists often failed to recognize and appreciate their professional competence. In a mental hospital, as in all social organizations, members develop particular attitudes toward others which may not be congruent with what others think they have a right to expect. Consequently, the process of institutionalization may be analyzed at two levels—the level of overt acts and the level of evaluative attitudes. It is, of course, true that the overt act itself often conveys a particular attitude of others, as is dramatically portrayed in acts of deference. It is, nevertheless, important to keep the two analytically separate.

Since these events were largely created by ambiguity and disagreement among Department personnel regarding the role duties of various professions, the concepts of role and role conflict were essential for their understanding. At the same time, however, there are serious limitations involved in the use of role concepts, requiring their supplementation with additional concepts. To understand these limitations, it will be well to explain in detail what we mean by social role.

Although there are differences in the precise definition given to the role concept,[20] most "role theorists," especially those much influenced by Ralph Linton,[21] make two important assumptions about social behavior.

First, they assume that behavior directed toward others is *prescribed* by social norms. This can be seen when the distinction between position (or "status") and role is made. A social position consists of a set of rules which define and prescribe the performances and attitudes which persons occupying the position are supposed to express toward persons in related positions. Such acts and attitudes are role behavior. For example, Linton stated that role consists of "the attitudes, values and behavior *ascribed* (prescribed) by the society to any and all persons occupying (a particular) status." [22] This prescriptive assumption is also reflected in the more social-psychological role formulations of Theodore Newcomb, who states: ". . . each position carries with it *definite prescriptions* toward behaving toward persons in related positions. Thus, the position of mother carries with it the implication of certain ways of behaving toward children, just as the position of store clerk carries with it certain ways of behaving toward customers, toward employers, and toward other clerks. Such ways of behaving toward others, which are defined for different positions, are called *roles*. . . ." [23]

The second assumption refers to agreement between role partners regarding the norms in terms of which they interact.[24] Role partners agree on the respective performances each should enact vis-à-vis the other, so that each knows what to expect of the other. The store clerk, for instance, has a right to expect certain actions from his employer (such as financial remuneration at the end of the week) and is obligated to perform certain actions the employer expects of him (such as waiting on customers); and vice

20. For two reviews of the uses of the role concept, see L. Neiman and E. Hughes, "The Problem of the Concept of Role: A Re-Survey of the Literature," *Social Forces,* XXX (1951), 142-49; and Neal Gross, Alexander McEachern, and Ward S. Mason, *Explorations in Role Analysis* (New York: John Wiley and Sons, Inc., 1958), pp. 11-18.
21. Ralph Linton, *The Study of Man* (New York: D. Appleton-Century Company, 1936).
22. Ralph Linton, *The Cultural Background of Personality* (New York: D. Appleton-Century Company, 1945), p. 18.
23. Theodore M. Newcomb, *Social Psychology* (New York: Dryden Press, 1950), p. 278.
24. On the assumption of consensus in "role theory," see Gross, McEachern, and Mason, *Explorations in Role Analysis,* pp. 21-44.

versa. Note, however, that norms do not require identical responses from role partners, but complementary responses instead. Clerks wait on customers while their employers supervise their work and reward them with pay; husbands provide for the family's economic welfare, while wives keep house and care for children. Role consensus, then, may be referred to as "role complementarity." [25] Role complementarity is actually an extension of the prescriptive assumption: not only is the role player's behavior prescribed by a set of social norms; it is also integrated with the behavior of role partners. It would seem that some degree of complementarity characterizes all stable social relationships. Otherwise, actors will rarely know what to expect of each other; their behavior will not be co-ordinated and will often conflict; they will likely despair of the situation and withdraw, terminating the relationship.

These formulations of "role theory" have proved useful in the description and analysis of many social situations. Concepts such as role and role conflict are especially useful for locating strain and tension in social relationships. Nevertheless, it would seem that the primary usefulness of "role theory" is restricted to highly structured features of social relationships. Relationships are structured—in the sociological sense—if parties are aware of, and in agreement on, their respective obligations to each other and each knows what to expect from the other. And when this condition exists, as we have said, the relationship is institutionalized. "Role theory" tends to view social behavior as resulting from this institutionalized structure.

As we have indicated, however, there is reason to believe that such conditions often do not prevail in modern mental hospitals. The present study, for example, focuses on situations in which evidence indicates the prescriptive and complementarity assumptions are not valid. In particular, we will be concerned with the analysis of individuals' reactions to these stuations—situations that are poorly institutionalized. Our interest, therefore, centers on a form of noninstitutionalized behavior. "Role the-

25. For a more elaborate discussion of role complementarity, see Talcott Parsons and Edward A. Shils, *Toward a General Theory of Action* (Cambridge: Harvard University Press, 1951), *passim*. It should be noted that there are other ways in which the term consensus is employed in sociology. For a discussion, see Irving Louis Horowitz, "Conflict, Consensus, and Cooperation," in *The War Game* (New York: Ballantine Books, Inc., 1963), pp. 147-69, esp. p. 148.

ory," containing the assumptions that it does, is not adequately suited for the analysis of this type behavior. For example, as a conceptualization of social structure, it does not contain the necessary conceptual tools for analyzing the process of structural development, of institutionalization.[26] How does one analyze, for instance, the process of role-*making*[27] with concepts which assume the existence of a role structure? It may be true that one can fully understand this process only if one knows the role structure in which the role-maker wants to become a part. Still, one cannot analyze this process of institutionalization only with concepts which are formulated primarily to give a generalized description of institutionalized social relationships.

In order to analyze behaviors that are noninstitutionalized, and at the same time recognize the existence of institutionalized normative orders (e.g., role structures), it is necessary to distinguish between normatively *oriented* social behavior and normatively *prescribed* social behavior. Human behavior is social insofar as the individual takes account of the behavior of others.[28] Such behavior is always influenced by a normative order, variously referred to as culture, norms, values, customs, and tradition. Indeed, sociological theories are grounded on this assumption: a person's social acts are always oriented to the culture, norms, and customs to which he has been exposed.[29] We recognize its validity in this book.

Role behavior, on the other hand, makes the additional as-

26. See Rue Bucher and Anselm Strauss, "Professions in Process," *American Journal of Sociology,* LXVI (1961), 325-34.
27. Ralph H. Turner, "Role-Taking: Process vs. Conformity," in Arnold M. Rose (ed.), *Human Behavior and Social Processes: An Interactionist Approach* (Boston: Houghton-Mifflin Co., Inc., 1961), pp. 20-40. For a concrete description of the role-making process, see chap. 4 below.
28. Max Weber, *The Theory of Social and Economic Organization,* trans., A. M. Henderson and Talcott Parsons (Glencoe: The Free Press, 1947).
29. Alvin Gouldner correctly points out, however, that some sociological theorists, viz., George C. Homans, begins not with the normative assumption but with the assumption of interaction. See Hans L. Zetterberg (ed.), *Sociology in the United States of America* (Paris: UNESCO, 1956), p. 35. Nevertheless, as Gouldner points out, the "interactionists" do not neglect the normative element in social behavior. Homans, for example, includes social norms among the four basic elements of the group. *The Human Group* (New York: Harcourt, Brace and Co., 1950). Also, in his theoretical analysis of "elementary forms of social behavior," group norms and values are important determinants of the individual's rewards and costs and, therefore, his profit. See *Social Behavior: Its Elementary Forms* (New York: Harcourt, Brace, and World, Inc., 1961).

sumptions of prescription and complementarity. Not only is behavior oriented to the normative order; it is prescribed by it and
based on consensus between the actor and the recipient of the act.
For example, nurses and doctors agree that the latter is in charge
of the patient, that he has authority over the nurse, and that the
nurse is to obey his orders. Norms define the nurse as the subordinate, insofar as patient care and responsibility are concerned.
Consequently, when a nurse carries out the doctor's order, she
follows a prescribed rule—her behavior is institutionalized.
There may be occasions, however, where she will try to elicit a
change in the doctor's order, an act which may meet with the
doctor's disapproval. Yet, she cannot demand this change because the doctor's role gives him authority which she must
respect. She must, therefore, influence him without challenging
his authority.[30] In such cases, her behavior is *oriented to* rather
than *prescribed by* the normative role structure.[31] Since we are
concerned with this type of behavior, we have had to supplement
role concepts with other concepts. One such concept is called
"power strategy" and will be defined in Chapter 2.

The author is aware that severe restrictions have been imposed
on the empirical applicability of role concepts. Also, discussion
has been restricted to that brand of "role theory" which has been
particularly influenced by Ralph Linton's early formulations.
Most "role theorists," no doubt, would agree that the prescriptive and complementarity assumptions are matters of degree.
Nevertheless, they do not provide the concepts for analyzing social behavior under poorly institutionalized conditions. We feel
that there is a static bias inherent in role formulations which
does not permit the conceptual clarity necessary to understand
clearly certain empirical processes which occur in an organization undergoing rapid institutionalization. They must be supplemented with more precise conceptualizations of the institutionalization process.

This is not to say that role structures, as we have defined them,
will be ignored. Quite the contrary. Indeed, as we have stated,
comprehension of the role concept is necessary for understanding

30. See, for example, chap. 7 below.
31. Max Weber was early to recognize the distinction between normatively
   oriented and normatively prescribed actions: "It is possible for action to
   be oriented to an order in other ways than through conformity with its
   prescriptions. . . ." in *The Theory of Social and Economic Organization*,
   p. 125.

the organization of this hospital, as it is for understanding any complex social organization. However, role structures are viewed as frameworks within which social behavior is enacted and toward which it is oriented, rather than its "determinants." [32]

32. Actually, "role research" often employs role structures in this sense. Strict adherence to "role theory" definitions, however, would require formulations which include the prescriptive and complementarity assumptions. On the point that the research use of role is not always consistent with theoretical statements about the concept, see Erving Goffman, *Encounters* (Indianapolis: Bobbs-Merrill Co., 1961), p. 92.

2 THE CONCEPTUAL FRAMEWORK

We have distinguished between normatively oriented behavior and normatively prescribed behavior and indicated that this study concerned itself with the former. It is also more concerned with the individual's reactions to the social structure and his attempts to modify it than with his socially-structured conformity. These problems will be given detailed analysis within an explicit theoretical framework.

The framework begins with the view that in the pursuit of his goals, the individual actor (ego) depends upon responses from others (alters). To perform his duties and achieve his objectives within an organization such as a mental hospital, one depends on the acts of others, for a social organization consists of a complex of interrelated activities. And when an actor is dependent on others, others have power over him.[1] Thus, one has power when he can facilitate (or interfere with) another's goal attainment and task performance.

In a perfectly integrated social structure, ego experiences few problems performing his tasks and achieving his goals. Alter's responses are "guaranteed" by a set of social norms which define his duties and responsibilities to ego. Having internalized these

1. See the following for formulations which also equate power with dependency. John W. Thibaut and Harold H. Kelley, *The Social Psychology of Groups* (New York: John Wiley and Sons, Inc., 1959), Chapter 7; Robert Dubin, *The World of Work* (Englewood Cliffs, N. J.: Prentice-Hall, Inc., 1958), pp. 29-48; and Richard M. Emerson, "Power-Dependence Relations," *American Sociological Review*, XXVII (1962), 31-41.

norms, alter feels obligated to perform activities that facilitate ego's goal attainment. (The same is true for ego and his action vis-à-vis alter.) This study, however, investigates those processes involved when alter fails to provide ego with the desired response. The concrete problems encountered by each group of mental health professionals are, therefore, formulated in reference to others' failure to perform desired actions.

We also investigate ways in which these persons react to others' noncompliance, particularly their attempts to influence others' behavior. In sociology, the concept of negative sanction (punishment) is often used to describe these actions. This concept, however, implies the existence of an institutionalized ego-alter relationship, that is, agreement concerning the behavior each should perform vis-à-vis the other. Consequently, alter's deviation from agreed upon definitions elicits a negative sanction from ego, and vice versa.[2] Furthermore, it is considered legitimate and appropriate to punish one who deviates. Thus, negative sanctions are a form of role behavior—behavior one is expected to enact. Parsons and Shils put the point this way:

> What an actor is expected to do in a given situation, both by himself and by others, constitutes the expectations of that role. What the relevant alters are expected to do, contingent on ego's actions, constitute the sanctions (positive and negative). Role expectations and sanctions are, therefore, . . . *the reciprocal of each other*. What are sanctions to ego, are also role-expectations to alter, and vice versa.[3]

Because the concept of negative sanction often carries with it the connotation of an institutionalized relationship, we will replace it with another concept. The concept we have chosen is "power strategy," sometimes referred to simply as influence attempt. A power strategy refers to ego's noninstitutionalized attempt to influence alter's performance of desired behavior. Ego's going to alter's superior to "make" alter comply is an example. To say that behaviors are noninstitutionalized means that they are not organizationally prescribed and the result of consensus. They are called power strategies because ego influences,

2. A. R. Radcliffe-Brown, *Structure and Function in Primitive Society* (Glencoe: The Free Press, 1951), p. 205.
3. Talcott Parsons and Edward A. Shils (eds.), *Toward a General Theory of Action* (Cambridge: Harvard University Press, 1951), p. 191 (authors' emphasis).

or attempts to influence, the behavior of others who have power over him.

It is, of course, recognized that much organizational behavior is normatively prescribed: one must conform to organizational rules and regulations which define participants' duties and responsibilities, as well as to requirements of superordinate-subordinate relationships. Therefore, actors must take normative orders into consideration in their attempts to influence. Indeed, power strategies can only be understood when viewed within the normative context of their enactment. But this does not necessarily mean that they are institutionalized behavior in *conformity with* the normative order. When attempting to influence another, it is true that the actor must not violate accepted values and standards of appropriate behavior, but this behavior may not be specifically prescribed by those standards. As in our previous example, a nurse may want the physician to change his plan of patient care, but she cannot demand this change because the doctor's role gives him authority which must be respected; she must influence his decision without challenging his authority. Power strategy is, then, precisely defined as an act designed to influence the behavior of another, but an act that is *oriented to* rather than in *conformity with* institutionalized normative orders. Power strategies are not the only reactions with which we will be concerned, but they are the most important.

Thus, while our primary concern will not be with institutionalized role structures, we will not be unconcerned about them either. In fact, the empirical relationships between types of power strategies (i.e., noninstitutionalized behavior)[4] and features of institutionalized social structures will be given detailed consideration. The concept of cost is employed to conceptualize these relationships.

Cost is defined as a "value forgone." [5] Effective role performance—an important goal for most professional persons—entails costs because one must forgo something to attain it. For example, role performance requires effort. Such effort is costly because the actor might have performed a more pleasant activity, or he

---

4. In light of our use of conceptualizations from George C. Homans, the reader may prefer to substitute the term "subinstitutional" for "noninstitutional." On the distinction between the institutional and the subinstitutional, see George C. Homans, *Social Behavior: Its Elementary Forms* (New York: Harcourt, Brace and World, Inc., 1961), pp. 378-98.

5. *Ibid.,* pp. 57-61.

could have done nothing. Usually a task can be performed in several ways, some of which are less costly than others, e.g., some require less effort than others. When the actor must perform his task one way, but conceives a more efficient (less costly) alternative, he forgoes a value—the better alternative. He thus incurs costs. The concept of cost is applied to two conditions, both of which stem from alter's noncompliance.

The first usage refers to alter's failure to perform the desired activity, such that ego is deprived of a value. This condition will be referred to as deprivation. Deprivation, then, always derives from alter's failure to perform activities desired by ego. It may result from alter's holding a different definition of his role than that held by ego.

Second, cost is also used in reference to the power strategy concept. When ego elicits the desired response from alter, he receives a value. Since there may be several ways to influence alter, some alternatives are likely to be more costly than others. For example, some may require more time and effort to execute. Or ego may not want to exert influence at all; he may want the desired response (value) without exerting influence to get it.

Three types of power strategies are identified according to the character of their costs. Some strategies are *cost inducing:* they are necessary to obtain desired values, but are accompanied by the actor's forgoing other important values. The cost of surveillance, for example, may involve more time and effort than one cares to forgo; other strategies may create the costs of psychological discomfort, such as embarrassment and anxiety; in still other cases, the actor may consider it beneath his dignity to have to influence others' compliance which he considers he has a right to expect. Influence attempts that eliminate or reduce the necessity for such strategies are called *cost-reducing strategies:* the imposition of rules on others' behavior to eliminate the cost of time, effort, and psychological discomfort is an outstanding example. The rule may control and stabilize the others' behavior and, therefore, guarantee the actor a value-producing response, thus eliminating the necessity for cost-inducing influence—such as maintaining surveillance, for example. Finally, a strategy is said to be *cost preventing* if it keeps the other from placing the actor in a cost-incurring situation. This implies that ego already has an established relationship with alter in which he receives certain desired values. There may be occasions, however, in which ego must exert influence to receive them. In such cases, it may be necessary to influence alter without arousing his resentment and consequent withdrawal from the relationship, thus depriving ego of important values.

In Part II, the relationship between this typology of power strategies and degrees of institutionalization is explored. Our argument is that cost-inducing strategies are likely to predominate when relationships are poorly institutionalized, followed by cost-reducing strategies which aim to institutionalize the relationship. Implicit in this formulation is the hypothesis that social norms function as cost-reducing agents in social relationships.[6] Cost-preventing strategies exist when relationships are on a relatively well-established and institutionalized basis, such that alter's withdrawal would be more costly to ego than his temporary noncompliance.

As stated above, an important objective of the professional person is the performance of his occupational or instrumental task. He is also likely to want professional recognition and acceptance from others, to want respect and appreciation for his work. Although both objectives depend on others' acts, others' responses in instrumental orientations are means to an end, while their expressions of respect and appreciation are gratifying in and of themselves. The distinction is equivalent to that between instrumental and expressive orientations,[7] and hereafter will be referred to as such. In both cases the actor is dependent on responses from others, and in this sense others have power over him. Their responses have value for him.

Since power is defined in terms of alter's ability to facilitate (or interfere with) ego's goal attainment, and since ego has two goal orientations—instrumental and expressive, it follows that alter may have two kinds of power. When he has the ability to implement (or hinder) ego's instrumental task performance, his power consists of *facilities;* when he is able to implement (or hinder) ego's expressive goal attainment, his power is called *rewards.*[8] Facilities refer primarily to such things as activities, in-

6. Thibaut and Kelley, *The Social Psychology of Groups,* esp. pp. 130-35.
7. On the distinction between instrumental and expressive orientations, see Talcott Parsons, *The Social System* (Glencoe: The Free Press, 1951), pp. 48-49.
8. For a discussion of facilities and rewards as bases of power, see Talcott Parsons, "Revised Analytic Approach to Social Stratification," in *Essays in Sociological Theory* (rev. ed.; Glencoe: The Free Press, 1954), pp. 402-4; and for a discussion of the relationship of facilities and rewards to instrumental and expressive orientations, see Parsons, *The Social System,* pp. 69-79.

formation, communication, etc., which ego considers essential for his instrumental task performance. Rewards, on the other hand, refer to alter's attitudes toward ego.[9] Alter may thus possess two qualitatively different types of value for ego.

On the basis of the instrumental-expressive distinction, Part III is concerned with the question: in what respects is the problem of eliciting rewards from the other a different kind of problem from that of eliciting facilities? This is essentially the question: in what respects does influencing the other's attitudes and sentiments toward you differ from influencing his overt acts toward you? In approaching this we will be especially interested in the phenomenon of social norms. In what respects is the institutionalization of instrumental acts (facilities) different from the institutionalization of expressive responses (rewards)?

Finally, several comments should be made regarding the concept of reference group which enters importantly into the analysis of expressive orientations and deprivation. Other writers have recognized that reference groups may perform two different functions for the individual—a normative function and a comparative function.[10] We propose a third reference group function.

A normative reference group provides the individual with social norms which he assimilates as his attitudes and which influence the definition of his role. A group from whom he especially wants the expressive rewards of appreciation, recognition, respect, etc., will be called an evaluative reference group; the group functions as a source of evaluation and appraisal for the actor, as confirmer and reinforcer of his status and self-image.[11] Therefore, an individual's evaluative reference groups have expressive power over him. Comparative reference groups, in turn, provide the actor with reference points through which he compares his rewards with those received by others. An evaluative reference group is the source of the reward; a comparative reference group

9. "The 'core' of the reward system is to be found in the attitudes of actors toward each other." *Ibid.*, p. 415. See also, "Revised Analytic Approach to Social Stratification," p. 404.
10. Harold H. Kelley, "Two Functions of Reference Groups," in Guy E. Swanson, Theodore M. Newcomb, and Eugene L. Hartley (eds.), *Readings in Social Psychology* (2nd ed., rev.; New York: Henry Holt and Company, 1952), pp. 410-14; see also, Robert K. Merton, *Social Theory and Social Structure* (rev. and enlr. ed.; Glencoe: The Free Press, 1957), pp. 283-84.
11. An evaluative reference group is similar to what Ralph H. Turner calls an "audience group." "Role-Taking, Role Standpoint, and Reference-Group Behavior," *American Journal of Sociology*, LXI (1956), 316-28.

is a group against whom the individual assesses the amount of reward he receives. Such assessment is often a relative rather than absolute matter. The actor's feeling of being rewarded or deprived may not be so much the absolute amount of reward he receives from some significant other, but the amount he receives in *comparison* to others. Two individuals receiving the same absolute reward may, nevertheless, assess their situation differently because their comparative reference groups differ. Individual A, who compares himself with others who receive the same or less reward, may be satisfied. Individual B, however, may compare himself with others who receive greater reward, and, as a result, experience *relative deprivation*.[12]

The reference-group scheme will not be used in the analysis of all four groups. Although it enters into the analysis of recreation and, to a lesser extent, clinical psychology, its primary usefulness will be found in the analysis of the expressive orientations of social workers.

The reader should note that this book's focus is always social psychological. The point of reference is always the individual actor, not the organization as a social system. The consequences of both alter's actions and ego's actions are always considered in reference to their value-cost consequences to ego. This analysis therefore differs from a structure-function analysis in that "objective consequences" are always in reference to the individual, not the social system. Also, the general description of the organizational structure and changes therein are always in terms of their value-cost relevance to individual actors.

12. On the concept of relative deprivation, see Robert K. Merton and Alice S. Kitt, "Contributions to the Theory of Reference Group Behavior," in Robert K. Merton and Paul F. Lazarsfeld (eds.), *Continuities in Social Research* (Glencoe: The Free Press, 1950), pp. 42-51.

3 THE SETTING

The Department of Psychiatry is affiliated with a 483-bed university teaching hospital, and occupies a six-story wing which is connected to the general hospital by a passageway. Seventy-two of the beds are located in three inpatient wards in the psychiatric wing. There are two open wards containing patients diagnosed as neurotic, on one of which alcoholics and drug addicts are also housed. The other is a locked ward, containing severely disturbed and psychotic patients who require close observation. A senior psychiatrist ("attending man" or "ward chief") and a chief resident are in charge of each ward. Inpatient "ancillary" services are psychological testing, social service, recreation, and occupational therapy. The Department also provides for outpatient and child psychiatric services. The only "ancillary" services provided by these two units are psychological testing and social service; exceptions to this are children who are occasionally housed on the inpatient service. A senior psychiatrist functions as head administrator on each of the three service units.

There are two general classifications of patients—"staff" and "private," based generally on the patient's financial resources. As a rule, psychiatric residents treat only staff patients while staff psychiatrists usually treat private patients.

In terms of numbers, psychiatrists are easily the top ranking group in the Department. There are twenty-four nurses, six social workers, ten psychologists, and one recreator, but sixty-two psychiatrists. Twenty-six psychiatrists are faculty members and thirty-six are resident physicians who are doing their psychiatric residency under the supervision of the Department's staff psychiatrists. The large professional staff and wide variety of services offered to patients indicate the therapeutic rather than custodial orientation of the hospital. The short average period of hospitalization per patient on the inpatient service—24.4 days—is a further indication of this fact.

An important feature of the Department is the emphasis on three stated goals—education, service, and research. Personnel vary in their opinions as to which of these receives primary emphasis. The head of the inpatient service states that emphasis is first given to the educational needs of residents, then to the patients, with research receiving the least emphasis. The heads of the other two service units also state that education comes first, one thinking that both research and education are "top dogs," with service last. Psychologists express the opinion that the service emphasis makes it difficult to do research. Similarly, a research-minded psychiatrist, who is involved in research with patients, thinks that "patient care takes first place," although teaching may sometimes be first; in any case, there is "no doubt" about research being last. The chief social worker, on the other hand, states that there is "no question" about service being last, with research and teaching receiving greatest emphasis.

Although there may be a lack of consensus on the relative emphases given to these goals, the heads of the three patient services, as well as the attending men on two wards, indicate that education is the major goal of the organization. Discovery of the over-all relative emphases is not the primary objective of this study. However, the presence of three organizational goals does create various problems for the four groups with which this study is concerned, and will be discussed in chapters below.

The "ancillary" professions are given a certain autonomy within the Department, but none is an autonomous unit within the general hospital. Although each has its own department and department head, all are administratively responsible to the head of the Department of Psychiatry, who in turn is administratively responsible to the Hospital Administrator and to the Dean of the School of Medicine. There is no such thing, then, as a hospital department of psychology, recreation, or social work[1] in the same sense that there is a Department of Psychiatry.

1. During the course of the study, a hospital Department of Social Work was established so that the psychiatric social workers were no longer administratively responsible to the head of the Department of Psychiatry. This change, and its effect on the psychiatric social workers, will be described in chap. 11.

Within the social work and clinical psychology groups, there is a chief social worker and chief psychologist for each of the three service units (inpatient, outpatient, and child). Each is responsible to the unit's psychiatric administrator as well as to the head of his own department. The head of the recreation department is responsible to the head of the inpatient service.

Thus, although "ancillaries" have their own departments and leadership positions within the Department of Psychiatry, none has an existence outside the Department; and all are ultimately responsible to psychiatry. The same, of course, is true of psychiatric nurses. Staff nurses are responsible to the head nurse of their individual wards, and both are responsible to the attending man, chief resident, and other doctors on their individual wards. In addition, all nurses are responsible to the psychiatric nursing supervisor who is also responsible to the attending men and the head of the inpatient service, as well as to the hospital nursing supervisor.

In some cases, members of an "ancillary" profession hold a joint appointment in the Department of Psychiatry and their academic department in the university, located only a few blocks from the School of Medicine. The recreator is a member of the university Department of Recreation and several clinical psychologists have appointments in the university Department of Psychology. Such appointments usually carry teaching opportunities and responsibilities in the university departments.

An important aspect of this hospital, as well as all other hospitals, is the phenomenon of "blocked mobility." [2] Individuals can never be promoted (or demoted) out of their present occupational and professional group. They may be promoted within their group, but a member of one profession cannot be promoted to another profession—a nurse cannot be promoted to a doctor, for example. "Ancillaries" may, of course, be promoted within their academic departments on campus, but as members of the Department of Psychiatry they remain subordinate to the medical profession.

Since "ancillaries" usually work with the resident rather than the staff psychiatrist, they are subordinated to the resident, for

2. On the mobility block in hospitals, see Harvey L. Smith, "The Sociological Study of Hospitals" (unpublished Ph.D. dissertation, Department of Sociology, University of Chicago, 1949); and William A. Caudill, *The Psychiatric Hospital as a Small Society* (Cambridge: Harvard University Press, 1958), pp. 7, 339-40.

it is he who prescribes treatment services for patients. This is not to say that "ancillaries" are "assigned" to individual residents; only that the performance of their work activities may be contingent on the resident's decisions. In some cases, the "ancillary" service is routinely performed (e.g., psychological testing); in other cases a voluntary referral from a resident is required. The importance of whether the service is routinely provided—its effect on the "ancillary"—will be analyzed in later chapters.

The large number of residents reflects the educational character of the Department. Residents usually begin their training experience on the inpatient service where they spend one year, spending the next two years on the outpatient and child psychiatric services. (Also, medical students spend a block of time on the inpatient and outpatient services each year.) Although each staff psychiatrist performs fifteen psychotherapy hours per week, mostly with private outpatients, resident psychiatrists perform the bulk of the treatment services.

Considerable autonomy is given to residents in their treatment of patients. Although psychiatric residents, particularly first-year residents, usually have had little experience in psychiatric treatment, they nevertheless perform the regular responsibilities of a psychiatrist: they treat patients and work with "ancillaries" and nurses as "the captain of the team." They are supervised, of course, by staff psychiatrists, but are permitted wide latitude in their treatment decisions, including their use of "ancillary" services. As one staff psychiatrist expressed it, "At this institution the patients have been defined as belonging to the resident." Consequently, the "patient is the resident's responsibility. . . . He makes the decision, not the supervisor." Professional ethics are also involved. "I'm not entitled to tell another doctor how to treat his patient. No doctor is entitled to tell another doctor who is responsible for the patient how to treat that patient—it's a matter of medical ethics." The resident's autonomy is not unrelated to the routine character of the "ancillary" service, and the "ancillary's" problem of controlling the resident's behavior.

PART II

INSTRUMENTAL ORIENTATIONS

4 THE RECREATION SERVICE: A CASE STUDY OF ROLE-MAKING

A variety of recreation activities such as square dancing, "cook-outs," parties, swimming in the university pool during the summer, and various games are provided for inpatient service patients. Each Monday, Wednesday, and Friday afternoons an activity is scheduled for all patients in the multi-purpose room, often referred to as the "recreation and occupational therapy area." A "week-end activity" for all patients, held on either Friday or Saturday night, is also scheduled for this area. Patients from all three wards may participate in activities which take place outside the hospital in the form of "cook-outs," swimming in the summer, and visits to points of interest in the region. Additional activities occur on individual wards during the evenings and other hours of patient leisure.

Except for the occasional part-time assistance of students from the university Department of Recreation, all services are provided by a middle-aged woman. This chapter will analyze the operation of this person.

The recreation area is located on the first floor of the Department. Patients are housed on the second, third, and fifth floors, so they must be brought down to the multi-purpose room for activities held there. Also, when she must communicate with personnel on the wards, the recreator must go to the wards and

29

see the personnel in person. Such physical isolation is importantly involved in a problem of time: the recreator works fifty-five to sixty hours per week but only wants to work forty.

When research began, a recreation service had been a feature of the Department for less than one year. Except for the last two months of this year, the recreator operated with neither a job description nor any formal organizational SOP (standard operating procedure). In the tenth month of this year a job description was written by the recreator herself. Consequently, until this time, there was no "charter" prescribing the duties of the recreation service nor the activities of other personnel upon which its implementation depended. The establishment of a recreation program was the recreator's responsibility, her superiors (psychiatrists) informing her that what she did was up to her.

> I didn't know the setting at all [when I first came]. I didn't have an orientation when I first came. No one thought of giving me one. No one said this had to be done; no one said you have to do this. I wasn't told anything, just that it was up to me to go ahead and do it. How I got established and what my program was, was up to me. . . . No one told me what I had to do. I was told that what I accomplished was up to my own initiative and ingenuity. They didn't know what I did. They didn't know what recreation did in a hospital.

Two important but related points are to be noted. First, the recreator is not entering a position in a social structure which is defined by traditional rules and norms. There has been no previous recreation program and those who hire her are not specific about what they want from such a program. Consequently, the definition of her role—her program—is not prescribed for her. Second, duties of other personnel to the recreation service are left unspecified. Thus, two essential conditions of a social role are not met: the presence of rules prescribing the actor's duties and responsibilities, and the complementary performances and obligations of others. The recreation service is not yet an institutionalized feature of the Department.

The focus of this chapter will be the recreator's attempts to make a role and become institutionalized. Analysis involves not only the description of her own role conception, but the responsibilities and duties of others implied in that conception. Hopefully, the analysis will throw light on the general process of institutionalization.

RECREATOR'S DEFINITION OF INSTRUMENTAL ROLE

As noted above, the recreator formulated an explicit definition of her duties ten months after entering the Department. The core of her self-defined role may be seen from a brief statement of her job description: "The need of the *patient* and the *doctor's* aim of treatment is the key to the *recreator's* planning." The purpose of the recreation service is to provide for the "constructive use of the patient's leisure" and thereby "assist the doctor in his care of the patient." What is to be "constructive" for the patient, however, depends on the state of the individual patient. Since the doctor is the one who best understands the patient's "needs," he must, therefore, instruct the recreator in how she may assist him. The recreator defines her role as a mediating one between the resident psychiatrists on the one hand and the patients on the other.

She states that during team meetings and ward rounds, residents should give her "referrals"—directives in handling various patients in recreation activities. She then observes patients during recreation activities and reports her observations to the residents in ward rounds and team meetings. To complete the cycle, residents should then indicate how their patients should be handled during recreation activities.

The activities themselves are defined in terms of the "spontaneous interests of the patients." They should be the patients' "spontaneous choice" and not the choice of the recreator. In addition, patient participation must be voluntary—patients should not be forced or ordered to engage in recreation.

Such then is the basic structure of the recreation program. Involved from the beginning are residents and patients; the recreator's role conception implies activities from these two categories of persons.

The recreator is also dependent on nurses, aides, and orderlies. The nature of her dependence, however, can be understood only after certain of her activities in reference to residents and patients are described.

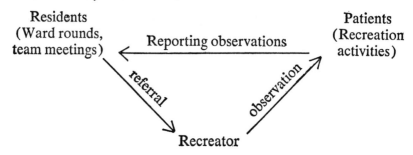

Figure 1.—Working Structure of Recreation Service

RESIDENTS: THE PROBLEM OF REFERRALS

Since recreation activities should be "spontaneous," they are not to be "ordered" or prescribed, in the sense that drugs, psychological tests, psychotherapy, or occupational therapy are prescribed. To be sure, doctors may prevent a patient's participation in recreation activities; for example, a patient diagnosed as "suicidal" will not usually be permitted to engage in recreation activities outside the hospital, such as swimming; in other cases, patients placed on "precaution" are not allowed to leave the ward for activities in the multi-purpose room. Nevertheless, doctors cannot prescribe recreation as treatment; there is no place for recreation in the doctor's order or prescription sheet. Consequently, referrals must be obtained verbally during ward rounds and team meetings. Since these sessions are held at the same time on all three wards, the recreator attends sessions on only one ward each day and gets information from nurses regarding what was said about various patients during sessions on the other two wards.

By referral, the recreator means instruction on how she might best handle the patient in terms of the doctor's aim of treatment once the patient decides to participate. She will want to know if she should encourage the patient to participate, if she should allow him leadership responsibility in recreation activities,[1] what his interests are, and what his basic problem is. On this basis

---

1. Leadership responsibility refers to whether or not a patient may be ward "social chairman." This position will be discussed under the section on the patients.

the patient will engage in recreation activities consistent with his therapeutic needs.

The recreator states that one area in which she has had difficulty getting established is in reference to residents' sending her referrals. Yet, observations of ward rounds and team meetings indicate that she gets referrals of the nature desired; residents instruct her in how she might handle their patients during recreation activities. Still, it is incorrect to assume that residents merely respond to the recreator's expectation of them.

It is noted, for example, that in many instances the recreator initiates the referral. Rather than the residents' voluntarily instructing her in how she might handle particular patients, she asks the residents for instructions. For instance, in one meeting she received five referrals, but in each case it resulted from her questions about patients: whether she should watch for certain changes in a particular patient who was receiving drug medication, whether she should allow one "extremely sick" patient to assume leadership responsibility (remain as a "social chairman"), or whether she should "support" another patient and "how much support" she should give him.

On the surface, questioning residents about their patients may seem of little significance—she is merely getting needed information about patients. Closer inspection, however, reveals that the recreator is influencing the residents' conformity to her definition of their behavior. Indeed, she is aware of this, commenting: "You have to do this [ask them questions] with the new ones. [Shrugs shoulders.] You have to do all of them that way. I have to keep asking them about their patients to let them know I'm around so they will use me." Since the residents do not voluntarily comply, she must influence their compliance. As she puts it, "I've got to motivate them somehow."

This suggests that the recreator thinks residents do not recognize her and the recreation service as permanent fixtures of the Department with a service to offer patients. There are other indications that this is so.

She sometimes questions residents merely to make them recognize that recreation services are available, and not to obtain a specific referral. For example, rather vague questions are sometimes asked. In one team meeting, she asked a resident, "What would happen if patient _____ were moved from the tight little group she is in to the larger group?" The resident smiled and replied that he did not know. The intent behind such questions may be seen from the recreator's remarks, made to the writer immediately following a session in which she had asked a resident, "What's with Mr. _____?" She asked the question, "So he [resident] would ask questions; so he would know I'm around."

The recreator's desire for residents to realize that recreation services are available for their patients is clearly indicated in her attendance at certain ward rounds. During the last two months of summer, ward rounds are used primarily for the educational purposes of new residents,[2] with team meetings the only regular source of exchange between residents and recreator (as well as nurses and other "ancillary" personnel). Rather than discussing every patient on the ward, one patient is thoroughly discussed for the purpose of resident learning. Since the recreator is "concerned with more than one patient—I have to find out about all of them," ward rounds may have little value for her. Some are considered useless.

> They [residents] are students, and this [emphasis on education] is something that has to be done. But the rest of us don't get anything out of it. I didn't get a damn thing out of that this morning. Did you notice the way resident _____ went on? I thought he would never shut up.

The interesting point is, although the recreator considers ward rounds of little value, she continues to attend them—sometimes when she fails to "get a damn thing out of" them. She does so in order to make the resident aware of a recreation service, "to let him know that recreation is there."

Team meetings are considered somewhat more valuable, but they too are limited: "You can't ever really count on them [being held]. . . . Like the one this morning with resident _____. I wouldn't have cared; I had plenty of other things to do; it's like that all the time. I'll be in a meeting and wanting it to end so I can get on with something else." Yet, she regularly attended team meetings because "It's important to contribute as teams as well as to let them know I am here. But," she continues, "I do this [letting them know she's here] in other ways

2. July is the beginning of the year in the residents' training program.

than just in teams and rounds. By talking to them . . . and introducing myself to new residents." Thus casual social relationships and team meetings, like ward rounds, are used to influence the residents' recognition of her so they will send her referrals.[3]

Because the recreator is often merely seen in these situations and does not become an active participant, in the sense that she solicits specific referrals, one might infer that she tries to influence the residents' tendency to refer solely by being "seen." This is especially true regarding her comments about "talking" to and introducing herself to residents when patients are not even discussed. Actually, she does think it is important to be "seen." "Sometimes you have to be seen. Being new, it's important to have them know that you are here."

One way of being "seen" is to establish oneself in a conspicuously visible place. This is what the recreator has done. Each Friday afternoon the Department has "Grand Rounds" which many members of the professional staff attend. The recreator volunteered to serve coffee during the intermission. The acceptance of this task allows her an opportunity to influence others' recognition of her membership in the Department. "That gives everybody an opportunity to see me; it gives me a chance to introduce myself to people so they get to know me."

Implied in the above are the processes which George H. Mead argued were characteristic of human behavior. The human act, according to Mead, is distinguished from the nonhuman act in that it is calculated to influence the other. Furthermore, in this act of influence, the actor "takes the role of the other"—he anticipates the other's response before carrying through the initiated influence act.[4] Accordingly, in her influence attempts the recreator takes the role of the residents, for she anticipates their reaction to her attempted influence. She asks residents questions, talks and introduces herself to them, attends team meetings and ward

3. Another technique the recreator utilized was repeatedly to introduce the writer in ward rounds, team meetings, and to individual residents, as a social researcher who was studying the recreation service. The recreator (voluntarily) informed the writer that she was glad to do this because it called attention to the fact that there was a recreation service in the Department.

4. George H. Mead, *Mind, Self, and Society,* ed. Charles W. Morris (Chicago: University of Chicago Press, 1934).

rounds, and establishes herself in conspicuous places, because she anticipates the residents' response to these acts: residents will come to recognize her as a member of the Department who has a service to offer their patients. They will consequently begin referring patients to her.

The preceding illustrates the recreator's problem in obtaining voluntary referrals and recognition from residents, as well as certain of her reactions to this problem. Such reactions should not be interpreted as role behavior, since role behavior refers to institutionalized duties and responsibilities that have been ascribed to a position (or status) in a social structure. The position of recreator, we remember, was without an agreed upon definition between recreator and psychiatrists. It is obvious from the residents' behavior that their definition of her role was not consistent with her definition. Her reactions are better interpreted as power strategies: noninstitutionalized responses designed to influence doctors to utilize recreation services—to comply with her definition of their behavior, that is, to provide her with referrals.[5]

Other strategies were also employed. One such strategy, the *tertius gaudens,* a term originally formulated by Georg Simmel,[6] is used in a broader sense than perhaps Simmel intended. Here it refers to an inferior's attempt to influence his immediate superior by going to the superior's superordinate and getting him to utilize his power in the interest of the inferior.[7] The recreator attempts to influence the resident by going to the chief resident.

This strategy is sometimes used in conjunction with asking questions in ward rounds. For example, the recreator asked a resident if a patient should be permitted to assume leadership responsibility in recreation activities. The resident thought not. The chief resident wondered if "other means" could be found "for this patient to express himself in OT and RT." At the end of this meeting the recreator initiated discussion with the chief resident, discussing further the idea that "other ways of permit-

5. The attempt to obtain recognition is also involved in the recreator's expressive orientations. This is fully discussed in chap. 8.
6. Georg Simmel, *The Sociology of Georg Simmel,* trans., edited, and with an introduction by Kurt H. Wolff (Glencoe: The Free Press, 1950), pp. 154-62.
7. Literally, *tertius gaudens* means "the third who enjoys" or "the third party which in some fashion or another draws advantage from the quarrel of two others"; see *ibid.,* p. 154, n. 13.

ting the patient to express himself might be valuable." After the meeting, she informed the author that she initiated this discussion so the chief resident would say something to the resident, to whom she addressed the original question, about using recreation services. Her reasoning was that after discussing with the chief resident other ways for the patient to "express himself while he's in the state he's in," the chief resident informs her "what he thinks would be the best way to relate to the patient" and how she "might handle him"; then, because the patient's doctor is the resident to whom she addressed the original question, "the chief resident will say something to him"; and he, in turn, will inform her how she might further help the patient through recreation activities.

Whether this was a successful influence attempt is not known. However, it clearly illustrates the recreator's attempt to use the authority of the residents' superior in an effort to get a resident to send her referrals. It also illustrates the complexity of the role-taking process. The recreator takes the role of the chief resident and anticipates that he will mention recreation activities to his subordinate, who will then make use of recreation services. Although the recreator overtly interacts with the chief resident in this process, symbolically she interacts with his subordinate. Her ultimate aim is to influence the resident, and although she does not overtly interact with him, she does role-take with him, as well as with the chief resident, for she anticipates how he will react to the chief resident's act, which she hopes to initiate.

Another way to influence the other is to define your own activity in terms of his self interest. For example, the recreator interprets her services to the residents in terms of recreation's treatment value for their patients. In this connection, she made arrangements with the head of the inpatient service to have an orientation session with residents during which she explained her functions and expressed the need for referrals. At this time, she introduced a new referral form which (hopefully) would become the method of patient referrals. A resident asked, "Do you want one on *every* patient?" The recreator replied:

> Just as you see fit. I'm the recreator and I plan the recreation activities, but you are the ones. We want to give you what you want, to help you where we can. We are a guest discipline; psychiatry is the host. We are here to help you.

Elsewhere, during this same session she stated:

> You are going to have to indicate the patient's condition, what
> his functioning is. . . . The referral slip is to aid in communica-
> tion—the communication problem of how to best help your pa-
> tient. You have to communicate to me before I can help you all.

Conversely, before the recreator can perform her self-defined
role, residents must send her referrals. Furthermore, it would
help them in their treatment of patients if they would.

The point is not whether recreation can benefit mental patients.
Rather, it is the fact that these statements were designed to obligate residents to initiate referrals voluntarily instead of having
to be influenced to do so. For once the resident accepts the interpretation that recreation can help his patient, he may feel obliged
to utilize recreation services and, therefore, to make referrals.

This inferred motive is not without foundation, as the recreator's remarks to the writer immediately after this session indicate.
She made these statements, at least in part, to emphasize the
point that recreation services were for the residents' benefit.

> I was glad that resident _____ asked that question about
> the referral slip. It gave me an opportunity to let them know that
> it was up to them. . . . I'm glad I had the opportunity to say
> this. It gave me the opportunity to let them know that it was up
> to them; that they will have to tell me what they want; to let them
> know that I'm only here to help them.

The referral slip, introduced about six weeks after the research
began, represents an important power strategy itself. Several interesting features surround its introduction. We will recall that
to receive referrals the recreator must rely on verbal communication in ward rounds and team meetings, some of which she cannot attend; moreover, she usually must initiate referrals in those
meetings she does attend, and sometimes asks questions merely
to make residents aware that recreation services are available.
The referral form would (hopefully) accomplish these things,
since it would "make the residents inquisitive." With a referral
form to fill out for their patients, residents would recognize that
recreation services were available for their patients. "They're

going to see that there is a recreation activity program. . . . They will know that there is a recreation activity program here for the patients." The referral slip, then, would replace the recreator's constant questioning activity in ward rounds and team meetings.

It would have replaced still another activity. Regarding her inability to attend all ward rounds and team meetings, the recreator notes that the referral form would be an "aid in communication" since it would "give the therapist an opportunity to let me know what he wants done for his patient." As it is, the recreator obtains this information *in*directly through the nurse, requiring the maintenance of close contact with nursing personnel on all wards. The referral form would establish a *direct* channel of communication with the residents. But since it would also *eliminate* the need for maintaining close contact with nurses, the referral form would replace these activities.

The interpretation that the referral form is a strategy designed to replace certain of the recreator's activities receives validation from two of her remarks. First, in response to the question of what she will do if the referral form is not used by the residents, she replied, "I will have to resort to nurses, and what I'm doing now." Second, she stated, "Yes, you can put it that way," when asked if the referral form were going to take her place.

Hence, the introduction of the referral form is definitely a power strategy, for it is an attempt to obtain necessary facilities (referrals) from residents. But it is one that would *replace other strategies* that require her presence. And if the referral form were accepted and used, it would be more efficient than the other strategies since it could be used with greater economy—it would save the recreator time and effort.[8]

This form may be considered in a more general sense, in terms of the process of institutionalization. Institutions, we recall, are rules (norms) defining the conduct of persons who are in continuous interaction in such manner that each knows what is expected of the other, and both feel that each should live up to these socially defined expectations. With the referral form, the recreator attempted to put her relationship with the resident on an institutionalized basis. It would have defined the recreator's expectations of the resident; the recreator also has the seed of

8. The referral form was never used by the residents.

morality (i.e., the "should") present in the notion that her services are to help the doctor's patient (and, therefore, the doctor should make use of them).

The residents' acceptance of the referral form would have certainly institutionalized the resident-recreator relationship, at least insofar as patient referrals are concerned. But as Everett Hughes has said, institutions "do not spring full-formed from the head of Zeus. Before they are institutions they are institutions in process." [9] To be revealed is the process which gives rise to this particular (potential) institution.

Obviously, the referral is an attempt to facilitate the recreator's aim of obtaining referrals; in this sense it is conscious and utilitarian in purpose. [10] This does not explain why she introduced it, however, because she was already using consciously utilitarian techniques to obtain referrals. But these methods were costly. We have defined cost as a value forgone: the forgone value may be another activity which is considered more valuable; it may be an activity which must be performed, but which is considered unnecessary or undesirable; it may be doing nothing; or it may be the time and energy involved in performing an activity. The time required to check with nursing personnel on those wards where the recreator does not attend ward rounds and team meetings is, therefore, a cost. To attend ward rounds and team meetings which are of limited value is also costly because a value is forgone: she has "plenty of other things to do"; she wants it to end so she "can get on with something else." [11] The referral form would have reduced such costly activities.

The recreator's actions also throw light on the function of moral principles implied in social norms. Note that she appealed for the acceptance of the referral form on the grounds that recreation services helped the residents' *patients*. Hence, she appealed to an impersonal agent to get it accepted. If residents had accepted (i.e., "internalized") the belief that her services could help their patients, and that this could be done through the use of the referral form, recreation services would be established on

9. Everett C. Hughes, "Institutions," in Robert E. Park (ed.), *An Outline of the Principles of Sociology* (New York: Barnes and Noble, Inc., 1939), p. 286.
10. Which William G. Sumner claimed to be a primary characteristic of institutions. See *Folkways* (Boston: Ginn and Co., 1907).
11. See above, pp. 34-35.

a moral basis. The residents would feel morally obliged to use her services—via the referral form, thus reducing her need to exercise costly informal personal influence. Simmel puts the point this way:

> In the morality of the individual, society creates for itself an organ which is not only more fundamentally operative than law and custom, but which also spares society the different sorts of costs involved in these institutions. Hence, the tendency of society to satisfy its demands as cheaply as possible results in appeals to "good conscience," through which the individual pays to himself the wages for his righteousness, which otherwise would probably have to be assured to him in some way through law or custom.[12]

This analysis suggests that the cost-reducing function of institutionalized social norms involves a more basic phenomenon than the one to which Simmel refers, however. Simmel refers to the costs of applying the sanctions of law and custom when the "organ" of morality is not operative in the individual. For the recreator, law and custom was not yet a reality, but she was in the process of trying to make a reality of the referral form. Had she been successful, she would have placed her relationship with the resident on a "legal" basis. Short of this level, the costs which are spared appear to be not the application of law and custom, but influence attempts and power strategies instead.

Clearly, the referral form was an attempt to introduce a formal rule into the recreator-resident relationship which would have *eliminated costly activity:* the costs of continually checking with nurses on all three wards; the costs of questioning residents in ward rounds and team meetings (the referral form was to make residents "inquisitive" and would let them know a recreation program was available); the cost of attending meetings that were of limited value; and possibly other costly activity (e.g., introducing herself and being "seen"). Seen from this perspective, then, the referral slip would have established a social rule replacing "the necessity for and the costs of the exercise of direct, informal, personal influence." [13]

12. Georg Simmel, "The Number of Members as Determining the Sociological Form of the Group," trans. by Albion W. Small, *American Journal of Sociology*, VI (1902), 19, n. 1.
13. John W. Thibaut and Harold H. Kelley, *The Social Psychology of Groups* (New York: John Wiley and Sons, Inc., 1959), p. 147.

This illustration suggests that the process of institutionalization may involve two distinct steps: (1) A stage in which power strategies are used, but which must be continued because no obligation has been received from the other party to act in accordance with the definition applied to his behavior. Such actions are called "implementing strategies" but they are also classified as "cost-*in*ducing strategies." (2) The introduction of a formal rule which, when accepted by the other, eliminates the need for strategies that are utilized in the first stage. In such cases, the introduction of a rule (norm) is defined as a "structural strategy" which is, at the same time, a "cost-*re*ducing strategy."

This hypothesis questions Homans' statement that "the verbal statement of a rule is the first step in the making of an institution." [14] The statement of a rule may be the second step, or at least a step subsequent to cost-inducing activity which results from others' failure to provide the actor with needed activities. The first stage is a cost-incurring one; this gives rise to the verbal statement of a rule.[15] Nevertheless, the above example illustrates another of Homans' remarks: "Structure is not a given: it is itself the result of social process." [16]

The referral form is also a clear-cut instance where one strategy may be used in conjunction with other strategies. In attempting to get the referral form accepted by defining her services in terms of the residents' interest, the recreator utilized one strategy to implement another. A more striking example is the strategy of *tertius gaudens* to "motivate" residents to use the form after she had introduced it. A few days after she had introduced it, the recreator was asked if she thought the residents would use it.

> I think so. It's up to me to motivate them. I've got to get them to co-operate. What I'll do is put one in the chief resident's mail box. I have a good relationship with him; he thinks I'm doing good work. When he sees it, he will fill it out and mention it to the residents.

14. George C. Homans, *Social Behavior: Its Elementary Forms* (New York: Harcourt, Brace and World, Inc., 1961), p. 59.
15. Because of man's ability to anticipate, however, the first stage may not appear. By anticipating the costs involved in the first stage, human actors may introduce rules and norms controlling (i.e., institutionalizing) the other's behavior without actually experiencing the costly effect of implementing strategies.
16. Homans, *Social Behavior: Its Elementary Forms,* p. 99.

To sum up the above analysis, the recreator was consistently deprived, in the sense that residents did not voluntarily comply with her definition of their role. She had to exert influence to coerce their compliance, but this was accompanied by much time and effort: she had to attend ward rounds and team meetings, she had to ask questions and make efforts to meet and introduce herself to new residents, and she had to maintain relationships with nurses so she would know what occurred in ward rounds and team meetings that she missed. She had to do these things partly because there were three wards and because of her spatial separation from the wards. But equally important was the fact that residents were not voluntarily responding as she wished. To put it differently, a strong normative "bond" was absent from the recreator-resident relationship, insofar as referrals were concerned; from the recreator's viewpoint, the relationship was not institutionalized. The introduction of the referral form was an attempt to routinize, stabilize, and control—in a word, institutionalize—the residents' behavior.

Probably many of the above problems would have been solved if the recreator had permitted recreation activity to be entered in the doctor's prescription (order) book. There are two important considerations to be noted in her unwillingness to do this. One stems from the occupational value placed on the spontaneous nature of patient recreation. Consequently, recreation activities cannot be "ordered" or prescribed, and the recreator has openly objected to recreation activities' being placed in the order book.

Second, not to be placed in the order book permits the recreation service to operate as an "independent" profession, in the sense that it is not subject to the doctor's authority—doctors cannot "order" or prescribe recreation for patients. Indeed, the recreator states that no one has authority over her except the head of the inpatient service and the head of the Department. While there are no data indicating that this is the recreator's *motive* for keeping recreation out of the doctor's order book, it is, nevertheless, one of its *consequences*.[17] If recreation remains out of the order book because of the recreator's desire to be "independent" of the doctor's authority ("orders"), it is a value achieved at a high cost.

17. On the distinction between motive and objective consequence, see Robert K. Merton, *Social Theory and Social Structure* (rev. and enlr. ed.; Glencoe: The Free Press, 1957), pp. 23-25.

PATIENTS: THE PROBLEM OF "SPONTANEITY"

Obviously, to "allow for the constructive use" of the patients' leisure entails patient participation in recreation activities. Such participation, it is recalled, should be the "spontaneous choice of the patients": "It is their recreation program. It is to be their free choice of their leisure as long as it's not injurious to their welfare as patients." The emphasis is not on the recreator demonstrating her ability and skill—"We are not concerned with demonstrating our ability in recreation activities." Neither should she plan activities for the patients: "Don't plan for them. We don't plan for the patients; we plan with them."

Since there are three wards containing seventy-two patients, it is impossible to plan with all patients. Therefore, the recreator plans with the patients through the social chairmen from each of the three wards. A social chairman and co-chairman are elected from each ward in weekly patient meetings, supervised by the chief resident and charge nurse of the ward. Through these patients the recreator attempts to plan activities consistent with the interests and desires of the patient population.

According to the recreator, social chairmen are to sound out the recreation interests of the patients on their respective wards. They then meet with the recreator, inform her of the patients' interests, and she and the social chairmen will plan the activities accordingly. Social chairmen are then to relay the plans to the patients on their respective wards. Such is the recreator's definition of the social chairmen's "role responsibilities." There are indications, however, that the social chairmen do not voluntarily respond in accordance with this definition, nor do they always know that these "responsibilities" even exist.[18]

In some instances, social chairmen do not show up for meetings with the recreator, in which case the recreator must go to their ward and get them or else plan with them separately after the meeting. Their lack of knowledge regarding their "responsibilities" can be illustrated by one instance when the recreator had to go to the social chairman's ward for her. Upon being asked what she had planned for the week-end activity and what the

18. For a discussion of the problem of getting patients to participate actively in "their" programs, see Robert G. Brown, Harvey L. Smith, and Earl Somers, *Experiment with a Patient-Planning Organization* (Chapel Hill: Institute for Research in Social Science, 1961).

patients on her wards wanted to do, the social chairman replied that she did not know, nor did she know that she should have done anything.

Even if the patients do attend the meeting, it is no indication that they know what they should do. In one meeting, for instance, the social chairmen revealed that they did not know recreation activities were to be the patients' "spontaneous choice." They indicated instead that they considered it the recreator's responsibility to inform them of what *she* had planned. For example:

Recreator: What does your ward have planned for Saturday night?

Social Chairman: What do you have in mind?

Recreator: Whatever you want to do. It's your recreation program; you can do whatever you would like to do.

This patient had obviously not accepted one of the recreation program's basic values—the premise that recreation is the patients' own program, that recreation activities are to be of their own choosing.

When patients do not share the recreator's definition of their "responsibilities," she must influence them by "suggesting" things to them. During one meeting, for example, she asked the social chairman from Ward X what the patients wanted for a week-end activity. The patient indicated surprise at the question and stated that she did not know what the patients on her ward wanted to do. The recreator responded: "It might be a pretty good idea if you found out right away. I was just thinking that you had better do it today [because] we'll have to know about it in time to make the arrangements." The patient's reply, "Shall I just ask them?" indicates that the recreator's definition of the patient's "role" was not shared by the patient. Consequently, the recreator reacted by defining the situation for the patient, even to the point of suggesting how the patient might perform this responsibility: "Why don't you bring it up tonight at your meeting? Say something to Mrs. _____ [another patient]. She'll have some ideas."

On other occasions, the recreator makes suggestions regarding the activity itself. In one meeting, after informing the social chairmen that they can do "whatever (they) wish," she asked: "Do you want a party? A square dance?" The patients responded:

"We'll ask them." A little later the recreator suggested a ping-pong tournament involving all three wards. The patients accepted.

After the meeting, the social chairmen are supposed to inform other patients of recreation plans. Here, again, the recreator must define the situation for them. After an activity had been discussed and adopted, the recreator pointed out the social chairman's responsibility to inform other patients about the arrangements—"You should inform your folks." Once more, social chairmen sometimes fail. An evening activity had been scheduled for outside the hospital. That afternoon the recreator went to Ward Y to find out from the social chairman how many patients from her ward would go. The social chairman did not know. She had not mentioned it to fellow patients. Consequently, the recreator had to take time and ask each patient.

All of this reveals that patients, as social chairmen, often do not voluntarily and spontaneously comply with the recreator's definition of their "role responsibilities." Although this particular problem was not investigated, there are probably several reasons why they do not.[19] First, patients are mentally ill and are, therefore, frequently incapable of accepting and carrying out responsibilities associated with ordinary social roles. "Responsibilities" of the social chairman role are no exception. Second is the problem of patients' defining their relationship with the staff as one of dependency.[20] As the above indicates, patients tend to expect the recreator to plan for them. Third, few patients are in the hospital more than three weeks and rarely occupy the position of social chairman for more than one week. It is possible that social chairmen are not around long enough to know what the recreator expects from them. In any case, and this is the important point, their failure to perform social chairman responsibilities has important consequences for the recreator.

The first consequence is the necessity to influence patients to comply with her expectations of them. She must make suggestions, visit their wards and plan with them individually, or make special trips to wards and get patients who fail to appear. In addition, because the social chairmen are inadequate liaison agents between the recreator and the patients, the recreator must maintain relationships with the patients directly and not just

19. For a discussion, see *ibid.,* pp. 21-32.
20. *Ibid.,* p. 25.

through the social chairmen. She must do this so that patients will know that recreation facilities are available for their use, as well as to sound out the patients' interests. This, however, is *costly* because it is time consuming.

> I just don't have enough time. There's no time to get up on the wards to talk to the patients, to motivate them. There is a need to have relationships with the patients. You can't just leave it with the social chairmen; they're sick people. You have to say something to the patients; you have to keep letting them know you are here and that recreation is available to them.

Thus, inadequacies in the "role" performance of the social chairmen result in the recreator's maintaining continual contact with all three wards, reminding patients that recreation equipment and facilities are available, and having to "speak" and "talk" to them about recreation activities (to "motivate" them). Not only must she "remind" them of and "speak" to them about recreation activities; she must define for them their "responsibilities" to communicate their "spontaneous choices" to the social chairmen. On one occasion, for example, a group of patients from Ward Z asked the recreator what she had planned for them for the week end. She replied: "I don't know, whatever you want. I hope you have told Mrs. —————— [ward social chairman] what you want." Here the recreator is not merely "reminding patients that recreation is there." She is reminding them of their "responsibilities" to the social chairman.

Finally, once patients appear for the recreation activities (in the multi-purpose room), some may not voluntarily participate, preferring to watch instead. On such occasions the recreator mingles with patients and encourages them to participate.

These various modes of reacting to the patients' lack of "spontaneity" are influence attempts, attempts to get patients to behave more in accordance with the recreator's definition of how they should participate in recreation. Her need to "motivate" and influence patients reflects the same problem she encountered with residents. Instead of patients' voluntarily responding according to her definition of their behavior, she must influence them to do so. But to influence ("motivate") patients is not without its cost in time and effort. Consequently, it should be desirable to dispense with these influence attempts, provided other measures are discovered which would secure a satisfying and consistent response from patients. In other words, the recreator would profit if she could *replace* these time-consuming strategies with a more efficient strategy, analogous to the referral form. A formalized procedure must be ruled out, however, for it is contrary to the principle of "spontaneity." Her cost-reducing strategy is the utilization of nursing personnel in the recreation program.

NURSING PERSONNEL: A COST-REDUCING MECHANISM

Although the recreator conceives her role as a mediating one between the doctor on the one hand and the patient on the other, nursing personnel [21] play an important part in her program. A first indication of this is the recreator's statement that in recreation "the ideal situation occurs when the recreator is not even here." This means, for one thing, that nursing personnel should participate with patients during regularly scheduled activities in the multi-purpose room. They should also participate in and help patients plan activities on the individual wards during the evening and other portions of the patients' leisure.

In this, the recreator states that she is "assisting the nursing personnel in their interpersonal relationships with the patients." "Much of their work is routine; much of it isn't directly beneficial to the patient. . . . I've got to give these people help in these other (recreation) techniques. . . . These people are supposed to be with the patients and doing with them; and I've got to help them do it." Since nursing personnel are in constant contact with patients, she feels they need to do something with patients other than "just sit." Also, participating with patients in activities off the ward has additional value for nursing personnel. They are responsible for the patients and for keeping doctors informed about the patients' behavior during the course of the day; however, if they do not accompany the patients to recreation activities, they are not going to know "anything about how the patient is behaving."

Participation of nursing personnel must be viewed in terms other than its utility for nursing personnel. The recreator states that because she cannot be on all three wards all the time, nursing personnel must help patients in recreation activities. This is an economy measure, for she will not constantly have to arrange

21. The term "nursing personnel" is used to refer to aides, orderlies, and practical nurses as well as registered nurses.

for recreation activities on individual wards. If nursing personnel "are on the ball and get something cooking, I don't have to bother with it. If I don't have this kind of situation, I have to keep going up there."

The recreator's dependence on nursing personnel occurs in contexts other than their "interpersonal relationships" with patients. We recall that the recreator must go after social chairmen or else plan with them separately, if they do not appear for a committee meeting in the multi-purpose room. If nursing personnel bring the patients to the meeting, however, they save the recreator time. In commenting on having to go after one social chairman, she states that if someone from the nursing personnel had brought the patient down to the meeting, she "wouldn't have had to go up to Ward Y and find the social chairman, Mrs. _____. It didn't take but fifteen minutes, and it wasn't much trouble, as you saw, but these things build up."

Once the social chairmen are in the meeting, it is important also that the nursing personnel remain, primarily so that they can communicate the plans for recreation activities to the charge nurse. Patients cannot be trusted to do this.

> You can't depend on what they say. . . . Even if they do get it [the plan] right, the charge nurse [on the ward] can't depend on this. That's why I want a nurse there. I have to continually check on the ward if I don't get things communicated to the charge nurse.

During the social chairmen meetings, the nursing personnel are of further use in making "suggestions" to patients.

> It's always good for some of the other personnel to come down with them. Mrs. _____ is especially good. She is so enthusiastic and full of suggestions. She'll always help the patients come up with something. She usually knows what the patients on her ward want.

Regarding the over-all patient group, the nursing personnel are important in additional ways. The recreator, for example, may have planned an activity with the social chairman, but unless nursing personnel accompany them to the place of the activity (e.g., multi-purpose room), the recreator must go to the wards for them. Nursing personnel are also useful because they can keep patients informed of recreation facilities, can "explore" their interests, and can "suggest" recreation activities to them.

It is apparent that many of the activities desired from nursing personnel are time-consuming activities which the recreator must often perform. The nurses' time-conserving function becomes especially apparent when they do not perform these activities. Then "I have to fill in the gaps. And I don't have time." By filling in the gaps she means, for example:

> Like having to go upstairs yesterday. I had to go and get the social chairman on Y. I had to go up on X and talk to the patients [about the availability of recreation, what they wanted to do, etc.]. This wasn't any trouble and it didn't take a lot of time, but I could have been doing something else.

This process of filling in "the gaps" must be considered from a viewpoint other than the recreator's performance of certain activities when "things don't happen." It also indicates the recreator's use of nursing personnel to "fill in the gaps" (i.e., to keep things from not happening), so she can be "doing something else" (a value forgone). Activities such as helping patients plan, suggesting things to them, seeing that social chairmen attend their meetings, relaying information to wards—all must be performed if the recreation problem is to operate. They also take time. Consequently, time is saved if nursing personnel perform them for her. Otherwise, "these things don't happen." More correctly, they do happen, but the recreator has to do them. So interpreted, the process is one in which the recreator uses nursing personnel to perform her own activities.

The above brings into sharp focus the similarity between this process and the introduction of the referral form. Both are cost-reducing strategies: each is so designed that its success would reduce the recreator's need to perform time-consuming strategies. There is a concrete difference in the two strategies, of course. For the resident, she attempted to mediate the relationship with a slip of paper, whereas she employed other personnel to mediate her relationship with patients. Interpreted analytically, however, in terms of certain social-psychological properties possessed by each, both perform the same (potential) social-psychological function. From the perspective of their function as cost-reducing mechanisms, paper and people are interpreted as performing the same function, or being potentially capable of so doing.[22]

The dependence of the recreator on nursing personnel is of

22. Potentially, since the referral form was never accepted by the residents.

further interest because nursing personnel are not specifically mentioned in the recreator's job description, except to note that recreation activities are to be co-ordinated with the plans of the charge nurse. Their only mention is the notation: "Personnel attending activities are encouraged to participate rather than just being observers." Hence, many of the above features might be considered elements of the so-called "informal," as opposed to the "formal," organization of the recreation service.[23] Merely to label them, however, ignores the influence process and the important function involved in these "informal" activities.

It also fails to specify how the recreator tries to establish these activities and what she does to keep them established. She cannot "order" nursing personnel to perform them because she has no authority over them. Commenting on their participation in recreation with patients, she states, for example, "If they don't want to, they don't have to." This suggests that the recreator, not having any authority over nursing personnel, must get them to *want* to participate.

One thing she has done is teach aides and orderlies various games; for example, she has introduced a bridge class for them. Her reason for choosing bridge is as follows:

> I know it's a status factor with them, but it helps me too. A lot of the patients like to play bridge, so I'm not just teaching aides and orderlies to play for the fun of it. I'm doing it so they can play with the patients. It helps me this way.

Thus, the recreator offers the low prestige aides and orderlies prestige reward in *exchange*[24] for their participation in recreation activities with patients.

The recreator also shows respect and regard for the nursing personnel in order to influence their participation. When patients are in the multi-purpose room and are accompanied by nursing personnel, the recreator is careful never to request that a patient be returned to his ward. She leaves this decision with the aides and orderlies; this is their responsibility which she carefully respects. This is true even when she thinks the patient is too sick to continue participating. This, of course, confirms the nursing person-

23. For a statement on "formal" and "informal" aspects of complex organizations, see Robert Dubin, *The World of Work* (Englewood Cliffs, N. J.: Prentice-Hall, Inc., 1958), pp. 61-75.
24. George C. Homans, "Social Behavior as Exchange," *American Journal of Sociology,* LXIII (1958), 597-606.

nel's right to make certain decisions, and in this regard it is a means by which the role structure is maintained and status differences reinforced. It is *more* than this, however, as the recreator herself is aware. She states: "I had to give recognition to them in order to draw them in. For instance, I never take a patient from the recreation area." Here, again, the recreator attempts to establish an exchange with nursing personnel. In return for the reward of respect, she anticipates co-operation (participation with patients). Knowing the duties and responsibilities of the other, the recreator "takes the role of the other" and anticipates how he will respond to her acts of respect for his role responsibilities.

The strategy of according respect is also involved in what the recreator calls her "flexibility." By this she means that she adjusts her own plans and activities to those of the nursing personnel. If she goes to the ward to discuss recreation plans with the charge nurse and the latter is busy, she waits or else leaves and returns later. Even if she has a scheduled meeting with the charge nurse on the ward and the nurse is busy, the recreator talks to patients until the nurse is free. When nursing personnel are not prompt to bring social chairmen to social chairmen meetings, she waits until they arrive or else goes after them herself. If recreation plans conflict in any way with the plans of the nursing personnel, the recreator modifies her plans. For example, a week-end activity for all three wards had been arranged for a Saturday night in the multi-purpose room. The charge nurse on Ward Y informed her that patients on her ward would be unable to participate; there were several patients on "precaution" who were not permitted to leave the ward. As a result, all nursing personnel on Ward Y had to remain on the ward to care for patients. The recreator adjusted her plans and arranged for a separate activity on Ward Y.

These adjustments in her plans are necessary because she must adapt her activities to what "doctors think is best for the patients, and how feasible (her) plans (are) to the nurse." Doctors' orders and nursing plans are based on the needs of patients, which, of course, are unstandardized phenomena—needs of patients changing as they do. Thus, recreation activities are caught on what has been called the standardization-individuation dilemma characteristic of mental hospitals.[25] On the one hand there is the (recrea-

25. The dilemma felt to exist between organizational needs and patient needs has been formulated in different ways. Harvey L. Smith and Daniel J.

tor's) need for "order and stability," and on the other, the "individual needs of patients and therapists," [26] and, therefore, the work plans of nursing personnel. The need for more routine can be seen in the recreator's statement that although she realizes she "can't operate too inflexibly," she would like to "get a little more structure, a little less flexibility." As she puts it, she is "tired of moving with the tide."

In large part, however, she appears willing to accept the situation. She must do so because of the departmental "philosophy" that "the doctor is papa, the nurse is mama, and the patient is the child." Translated, this means:

> The doctor and the nurse are the ones legally responsible for the patients. . . . What they decide comes first, what recreation wants comes second. . . . I accept this. They're the persons who have the responsibility. . . . I have to recognize this. When I plan a program I take this into consideration. If my plans interfere with theirs, I have to make adjustments. I accept this.

By accepting (i.e., legitimating) this structure, the recreator does not try to make arbitrary decisions about recreation activities which involve nursing personnel. She discusses them individually with the nursing personnel instead. By accepting this structure of individuation ("flexibility"), however, she converts it into a power strategy. To return to the Ward Y incident:

> I could have gone and planned things without considering her [Ward Y charge nurse]. But you have to have respect for what the other person has to do and that recreation is in the leisure, in the free time of the patients. You keep those things in mind. You will never get anywhere if you don't—no one will co-operate with you. You can't go upsetting their work schedule.

Thus, a structure of individuation which impedes the implementation of recreation activities, or at least prevents their standardization, and which entails extra time and effort for the recrea-

Levinson refer to it as the "individuation-standardization dilemma"; see "The Major Aims and Organizational Characteristics of Mental Hospitals," in Milton Greenblatt, Daniel J. Levinson, and Richard H. Williams, *The Patient and the Mental Hospital* (Glencoe: The Free Press, 1957), pp. 7-9. Merton J. Kahne expresses the dilemma in terms of bureaucratic structure and personalized treatment; see "Bureaucratic Structure and Impersonal Experience in Mental Hospitals," *Psychiatry*, XXII (1959), 363-75.

26. Smith and Levinson, "The Major Aims . . . of Mental Hospitals," p. 7.

tor because she must modify her work plans, is utilized as a power strategy to elicit co-operation from the nurse. To adjust to "individuation"—to be "flexible"—is more than the legitimation and confirmation of the nurses' right to make certain decisions. It is also social influence.

The absence of routine in the recreation program is important. Other than the recreator's attendance at ward rounds and team meetings and the regularly scheduled afternoon activity, recreation program activities are not routine. The time and place of activities vary. Separate activities may be planned for each individual ward for one evening, whereas a trip outside the hospital may be planned for all patients on another evening. The weekend activity fluctuates between Friday and Saturday night. The time of the social chairmen meetings varies from week to week. Such variation means that the recreator must *personally* communicate the relevant information to the charge nurse on each of the three wards. A lack of routine requires that her relationships with charge nurses be "informal."

To complicate matters further, an activity may be planned for a time when the present charge nurse is not on duty. In such cases, the recreator must inform the charge nurse who will be on duty at that time. For example, when an evening activity has been planned in the afternoon, the recreator must wait until the charge nurse comes on duty to inform her. Also, she tries to inform the other nursing personnel who are to be on duty in the evening.

Because of the variation in her program and the need to adjust her plans to the nurses' work plans, the recreator cannot readily routinize the involvement of nursing personnel into her program. Instead, she must separately discuss her plans with the individuals who are to be involved.

Actually, the recreator feels that to try to operate "by definite policy or regulation" would defeat her purposes. To do so would be "imposing" her program on others, rather than "getting it accepted"—"You impose something on someone and you don't change his attitude." Consequently, personnel will co-operate because they have to—"because it's been imposed on them," but this means you do not get "the best co-operation in the world." One does not get others "to do these things because you order them, you convince them. You get them to accept what you do, you don't try to impose it on them. You impose it on them and as soon as you turn your back. . . ." To be able to turn one's back means that the surveillance of others' behavior to assure their performance of assigned tasks is no longer necessary.

Even if the recreator had authority over the nursing personnel, it would be hard to maintain surveillance of their behavior, except, of course, during regularly scheduled activities, because there are three wards. One of her objectives, however, is to have recreation activities on the wards in her *absence*. And if the nursing personnel accept her program, she *can* be absent—e.g., if nursing personnel "cook something up" with the patients, she need not be on the wards.[27] Thus, even assuming the recreator did have authority over these personnel, she would still need their acceptance of participation with patients as part of their role. Otherwise, she would incur the costs of keeping their behavior under surveillance: she would have to spend time checking to see if they were actually participating.

Consequently, rather than try to "impose" a formal program of activities on the nursing personnel, the recreator states that she "got to know" them first; she then approached them individually with the idea of participating with patients in recreation. In addition, because she was a newcomer, she had to get nursing personnel to recognize her as a member of the Department, just as she did residents. In so doing she again incurred the cost of time.

> There are three shifts of people who are working. The person who is working in the daytime this week, I may not get to see for two weeks. When I work twelve and fourteen hours a day, they would see me when they come on duty at 4:30. Being around so much it began to dawn on them that I was around and why I was here. . . .

She continues, however, "Some still don't know." She must keep "reminding" them that recreation equipment and facilities are available for patients.

The above analysis implies that the recreator implements her recreation program largely through face-to-face relationships with nurses. Because there is no formal structure to the recreation program,[28] the recreator must "individualize" her decisions by adjusting them to the work plans of nurses. Obviously, numer-

27. See above, p. 49.
28. With the exception of regularly scheduled activities occurring in the multi-purpose room.

ous face-to-face relationships are necessary. These relationships are to be viewed as strategies designed to get nursing personnel to perform various costly activities. Since it requires time to maintain face-to-face relationships, these strategies are not without their cost.

> I said that I was going to try to cut down on my time, but I don't know. There just doesn't seem to be anything I can cut out. I have to maintain my relationships with a lot of personnel—notes and memos won't work. I tried that when I first came here. I wanted the interpersonal contacts; I set it up this way purposely. . . .

Although setting it up this way *purposely,* the recreator seems to have gotten hooked on the bait of interpersonal relationships. Once they were established they could not be eliminated.

This analysis certainly reveals the recreator to be keenly sensitive to her social *milieu*. Her sensitivity to the role structure and her ability to "take the role of the other" and calculate how she might influence others are obvious. She knew what she wanted from others and purposely invented means to get it. The unanticipated consequences of her purposive social action apparently were not foreseen, however. She wanted "interpersonal contacts," but once she began them, she had to continue them. She therefore could not reduce her fifty-five to sixty-hour work week. And although formal procedures would save her time, they would not work because of her need for verbal communication. For example, in discussing the problem of time, she states:

> The trouble is we [recreation] need a procedure manual on the ward. But then people won't read it anyway. But we need something like that. But verbal communication always works better anyway.

This suggests that the structure of the recreation activities is dependent on the recreator's influence attempts and face-to-face relationships, rather than normative bonds between the recreator and nursing personnel. Nursing personnel, like residents, have not incorporated into their role the various activities upon which the recreator must depend. There is an additional source of data which indicates this is true.

We will recall the recreator's statement that "the ideal situation occurs when the recreator is not even here." In this connection, the recreator went on vacation during the latter phase of the study. A description of the operation of the recreation service in her absence could have determined the extent of the recreator's success in getting her "ideal" institutionalized. Such data are not available, however, for the importance of observing the recreation program in the recreator's absence was not immediately recognized. Nevertheless, the recreator's comments (after her return) about the "breakdown" in recreation activities are revealing.

Her explanation of the breakdown was that the patients were "not kept motivated" while she was gone—"There was no motivation behind the social chairmen and the patients." The day she returned "there wasn't any activity" because "no one had done any planning." Although she was asked to get an activity started, she refused to do so "because I didn't know all the patients, for one thing. I had been away, and there were a lot of new patients on the wards. You have to talk to and visit with the patients so they will get to know you. This takes time—you can't just set up a recreation activity and expect it to work. They [nurses] didn't realize how much was involved." Nevertheless, something "could have been done. I could have conjured up something. But I would have had to come early and stay late, and I'm not going to do this any more."

The interesting point is that the nursing personnel expressed a need for patient recreation, thus indicating their reliance and dependence upon the recreator and her program; but although something could have been done, the recreator did nothing. Her motive for reacting this way, in addition to not wanting to "stay late," can be seen from her response to the following question.

> Interviewer: Do you think that as a result of your being on vacation and refusing to set up an activity when the other personnel wanted it and saw a need for it that they more clearly saw your importance in the Department and your importance for the patients?

> Recreator: I don't know if this was all brought out, but it all pointed in that direction. I thought it was an opportunity to point this out indirectly without being direct about it.

Thus, the breakdown itself is turned into a power strategy. It was partially successful since "The result was when I didn't set it up, Ward Z planned their own activity."

Certainly, the nursing personnel's admission of their need for recreation expresses their value for the recreator and the recreation service. The breakdown might also be viewed as somewhat ego inflating to the recreator, since it implies that the functioning of the recreation program is dependent on her presence. To the recreator, however, it is "an evil."

> This is an evil—it's bad. Things should run just as smoothly when I am not here as they do when I am here. It shouldn't depend all on me.

In light of the previous analysis, it is understandable that such an event would be considered "evil." It symbolizes the recreator's failure to attain her "ideal," for she has not structured out certain cost-inducing activities by replacing her own performances with those of the nursing personnel. Consequently, as in the case of the resident, the recreation service has not become a firmly established and institutionalized social reality for the nursing personnel, at least in the sense that they are willing (or capable) of carrying out the responsibilities and duties of the recreation program in the recreator's absence. Their participation is still very much dependent on the recreator's power strategies. The recreator continues to try and make a role, rather than play one that is already made.

SUMMARY AND CONCLUSIONS

The detailed description of the recreator revolves around the process of role-making and clearly illustrates the empirical relevance of the power strategy concept. In the recreator's attempts to become institutionalized into the Department she employed two such strategies: implementing and structural strategies. The two types are characterized by different cost functions: implementing strategies are cost inducing, while structural strategies are cost reducing. This conceptualization breaks the process of institutionalization down into two separate analytic processes, or stages.

The introduction of the referral form illustrates the cost-reducing function performed by social norms. Data also reveal that nursing personnel, when viewed in terms of certain analytic structural properties, can be regarded as performing a similar social-psychological function for the recreator, although there are otherwise important concrete differences between them and the referral form.

In general, the structure of the recreation program was held together too much by the recreator's power strategies and "interpersonal relationships" and not nearly enough by normative bonds between the recreator and other participating personnel. Consequently, the recreator incurred much cost—represented by the number of hours she had to work per week. Also, the absence of this normative element resulted in a "breakdown" in the recreation program when the recreator was absent from the Department. Evidence indicates that the role of recreator is not yet an institutionalized feature of the Department.

This chapter has concentrated exclusively on instrumental problems involved in role-making. In Chapter 8 we shall return to the recreator and the expressive dimension of role-making.

5 SOCIAL WORK: IMPLEMENTING AND STRUCTURAL POWER STRATEGIES

The preceding chapter described the activities of a profession attempting to become established in the social structure of the Department of Psychiatry. It was hypothesized that implementing and structural strategies correspond to two distinguishable processes in the broader process of institutionalization. In the present chapter, these two concepts will be used to describe processes involved in the activities of a more established group. The analysis will be based on a study of psychiatric social workers, who, unlike the recreator, have been members of the Department for a period of five years.

Data are based on observations and interviews with eight social workers. Observations include a series of meetings between three staff psychiatrists and the social workers, in which the "relation between (psychiatric) social work and the Psychiatry Department" was discussed.[1] There had been a history of general dissatisfaction among the social workers, and the meetings were

1. The committee was entitled, "The Committee to Study the Relationship between Social Work and the Department." Hereafter, these meetings will be referred to as the "committee meetings."

to ascertain its source. The committee of psychiatrists met with the social workers once weekly for a period of eight weeks. During these meetings, as well as in interviews, social workers voiced the general complaint that it was difficult to work with residents.[2] This chapter will revolve around the analysis of this problem.

Importantly involved in this problem with residents is the fact that there is no formal definition of the social workers' functions. A job description exists, but it was written primarily by the social work supervisor and consists only of certain generally required skills, knowledge, and training. Social workers argue that psychiatrists should be more explicit about the specific functions of social workers. The following portion of the fourth committee meeting indicates the extent of this concern, as well as the psychiatrists' reaction to the social workers' request.

Social Worker X: Isn't the purpose of the committee to discuss the functions of social work?

Psychiatrist A: Yeah, I think that's the title of the committee.

Psychiatrist B: That's certainly part of it, but there are twenty-two psychiatrists who have different opinions about it.

Social Worker Y: What are they? That's what we want to know.

Psychiatrist B: They will differ. The functions will be different in inpatient, outpatient, and child. I don't care what other psychiatrists' opinions are; all I'm concerned with are the social workers who work with me. [B is supported by Psychiatrist A who states that he is not concerned with any social workers except those who work on his ward.]

Social Worker Y: We need to know the thinking of all the psychiatrists.

Psychiatrist A: Social Worker X, don't you know what I expect from you? [Social Worker X works on Psychiatrist A's ward.]

Social Worker X: You leave things pretty much up to me. What I do is left up to me. [X goes on to indicate that she pretty much defines what her duties are.]

Social Worker Y: You self-define it. But it's important to know what the psychiatrists' views are. I have never gotten [Depart-

2. In addition, social workers voiced various complaints concerning their salary, faculty status in the School of Medicine, and other prestige privileges. These will be analyzed in chap. 10.

ment Head] to specify, never any feedback from him. All he says is that he doesn't want any junior psychiatrists, but he's never specified what he means by it. That's not very helpful. Psychiatrists are usually very articulate, but not here. Why? I don't know. (Laughs.)

Social Worker X: Psychiatrist B, you seem to think it's a one-to-one thing.

Psychiatrist B: That's right. Work it out with each other [between the individual social worker and the individual psychiatrist under whom she serves]. I'm not saying that's the way it should be, but that's the way it is.

Social Worker Y: There are different areas in which the social worker works [child, inpatient, outpatient]. We must have some idea of what's expected of us in order to adjust to what's expected of us. The social worker doesn't know what the psychiatrist wants.

Psychiatrist B: The role will differ with the ward. It will differ if the social worker is in child psychiatry. The role will differ according to the group [team] she's working with. You must know what the needs of the social workers are, what the needs of the nurses are, what the needs of the psychiatrists are.

Social Worker Y: [Brings up the problem of new social workers.] When a new social worker comes in, she wants to know what her duties are. [Expresses the opinion that when a new social worker comes into a group, she does not know what her duties are unless she is told.]

Psychiatrist B: That's a new society.

Social Worker Y: No. [Reiterates that new social workers must know what their duties are.] It's useful to discuss these things with people you work for, but you have to have your duties specified for you.

Psychiatrist B: [Gives an example of a job he once had.] When I took the job, I asked what my duties were. I was told to go out and create my job.

Social Worker Y: That's true but. . . . When I first came here, I had a vague idea of what the role of social worker was. But I must have medical opinion. The social worker does not learn all she has to know in school. She doesn't learn how to teach medical students, how to work with residents. She just doesn't get it all in school. She must adjust to a special setting. Social work is done differently in different psychiatric settings. I want to hear from psychiatrists.

Psychiatrist B: You can't get an opinion from me for Ward X. You must work it out with the psychiatrist you are working for.

Social Worker Y: The social worker gets paid for a job, and she must know what that job is. There must be a generic base. We must know what the psychiatrists expect of us.

Social Worker Z: The problem seems to be, whose responsibility is it [to define the social workers' role].

Psychiatrist B: You cannot lay down a mandate that holds for everybody.

Social Worker Z: You must.

Psychiatrist A: It won't work that way.

Social Worker X: We need a job description. They [psychiatrists] call us junior psychiatrists, but the best I can make out of what they mean is casework treatment.

Social Worker Y: Social workers must have some explicitly defined duties. This is not merely an academic issue.

Two points deserve emphasis. There is, first, the unusual situation of one profession asking another profession what its own functions are, and further stating that it *must* know what the other "expects" of it. Next is the psychiatrists' psychological bias and individualistic frame of reference in their rejection of this request: things are to be worked out on a "one-to-one basis," "society" consists of the "needs" of its component individuals, and formal rules and SOP's ("mandates") have no useful purpose.[3] Thus, one party to a relationship expresses a need for an explicit definition of its duties (a need for a norm or rule); the other denies such a need. Only after describing the social workers'

3. On the psychiatrist's tendency to "individualize" social relationships and to act as if status differences did not exist, see Martin B. Loeb, "Some Dominant Cultural Themes in a Psychiatric Hospital," *Social Problems,* IV (1956), 17-20; and Martin B. Loeb, "Role Definition in the Social World of a Psychiatric Hospital," in Milton Greenblatt, Daniel J. Levinson, and Richard H. Williams, *The Patient and the Mental Hospital* (Glencoe: The Free Press, 1957), pp. 16-20.

definition of their role, as well as the problems encountered in its performance, can we understand their need for this explicit definition.

DEFINITION OF INSTRUMENTAL ROLE

The social workers' request is especially curious in light of interviews with them, as well as other committee meetings, in which they express definite opinions regarding their proper functions. All state that social work concerns itself with casework service for the patients' relatives, and all but one state that casework treatment is the primary duty of the social worker.[4] This role is one in which effort is made to understand how "family interaction" and the attitudes of family members have a bearing on the patient's illness, as well as handling relatives' anxieties, guilt, and fear surrounding the patient's hospitalization. Duties other than casework treatment were also mentioned: "environmental assistance"—vocational rehabilitation, financial aid, housing, etc. (2)[5]; "informal" teaching of residents (through the performance of collaborative treatment) (4); orientation lectures every six weeks and weekly lectures to medical students (4); psychotherapeutic treatment of patients (2); and research (2). Despite the performance of these duties, casework is the only function mentioned by all social workers. Social workers are clear that casework is their proper role. As one expressed it, casework is "the basic thing" among the social workers' duties. They feel they "have had experience in interviewing relatives" and "feel they are competent" in this area.

Therefore, the appeal for psychiatrists to specify their expectations of social work does not derive from the social workers' lack of clarity regarding their role. Before explaining this curious phenomenon of one profession asking another for a definition of its role, it will be necessary to describe certain difficulties social workers encounter in their attempt to perform the casework role.

4. Data for this statement are based on information volunteered by social workers or in response to the question, "What do you consider the duties of the social worker to be?"
5. Numbers in parentheses refer to the number of social workers mentioning this activity. These data are based on responses to the question above; see footnote 4.

RESIDENTS: THE PROBLEM
OF REFERRALS AND COLLABORATION

Like the recreator, most of the social workers' working relationships are with residents rather than senior psychiatrists.
Numerous complaints were made of the residents' failure to work
with them. One session of the committee meetings was devoted
almost entirely to complaints that residents refused to work with
them and collaborate with them. Social workers claimed that
residents *prevented* them from making, and would not *allow* them
to make, a contribution. Individual interviews during the meetings and shortly after their termination revealed more specific
complaints. These were (1) residents would not make referrals
to them; (2) residents would not work in a collaborative capacity
and schedule conferences with social workers once the latter
were on the case; and (3) residents thought social workers were
only concerned with cases needing financial assistance or as
someone to get "a relative off his neck," rather than someone to
discuss with him what "I know about the family and family relationships, and how this might have a bearing on the patient."
All complaints were not heard from social workers on each service, however. Inpatient social workers voiced all three, whereas
social workers in child psychiatry only complained about the
residents' failure to collaborate. The difference in complaints is
related to a difference in the structure of referrals.[6]

On the inpatient service, social workers may obtain a case
only if a resident refers it. This is due to the inpatient admission
procedure. Upon arriving for hospitalization, the patient and an
accompanying relative report to the Inpatient Admissions Officer;
the Admissions Officer assigns the patient to a ward and then
directs them to the Hospital Admissions Office and Finance Office, located in another section of the hospital; from there they
are sent to the patient's ward where they are met by the Resident
Admissions Officer, and subsequently seen by the patient's therapist; the resident therapist then decides whether to refer the case

6. The outpatient service will be eliminated from this analysis for two
   reasons. (1) During the major phase of the study there were no social
   workers on the outpatient service. (2) The one social worker who was
   subsequently employed on the outpatient service differed from the other
   social workers in that she did not consider her primary role to be casework. This deviant case will be analyzed in chap. 11.

for social service. Thus, the social worker rarely has contact with the patient or his relative during the admission procedure.

Social workers comment that this procedure is somewhat different from "traditional social work settings," where the social worker is the first person to see the patient (or client) when he comes to the agency. Consequently, case referral is more difficult than in other social worker settings.

> Social work in hospital settings is more difficult than in traditional social work settings. For instance, in family and community clinics the social worker is usually the first person to see the person coming for help. There the individual comes to me. Here, no one comes to me. I am not involved in in-take, so I don't usually see the family when the patient is first admitted. Only if someone is sophisticated, knows what social work is, and what the social worker is for, do they come to me. The doctor must ask them to come in for me.

Although a social worker occasionally gets a case "through the back door," during ward rounds the attending staff man may indicate that a social worker needs to be on the case. "As a rule we don't get on any cases unless they are referred to us by the doctor [resident]." Thus, referrals are not routine, but depend upon the resident's judgment. "The resident doesn't have to call us in on each case. It's not SOP. It's up to him whether or not he calls you in. He doesn't have to call us in." Once the worker is assigned to the case, dependence on the resident does not cease, for the casework relationship with the relative may require "collaboration" with him. Information from the resident on the progress of the patient's therapy is often necessary since, as one social worker expresses it, "Knowledge of the patient may help direct the casework relationship." Without such knowledge, the social worker does not know what the patient's problem is and how his relative may enter into his illness. When she is informed of such matters, she may help the relative more; and by helping the relative, she may be of greater assistance to the doctor "since the patient's problems are ones of interaction with relatives."

While collaborative information is desirable, inpatient social workers indicate that they sometimes have casework relationships without resident collaboration, but "ideally, it's better when we collaborate, when I can obtain this knowledge from the resident." Without referral, however, a casework relationship is usually not possible.

Referral procedure in child psychiatry is somewhat different. As a rule, casework treatment with the child's parents is required in all cases. Because of a shortage of social workers, however, and because psychiatrists want residents to have experience working with families, social workers may not perform this role. Still, unlike the inpatient service where "the decision as to who is to see the relative is made by the resident," in child psychiatry "the position is a little more firmly established." For here, "the assumption . . . is that the social worker will be working with the relative," if there is a social worker available. Consequently, case referral to the child social worker is not dependent on the resident's judgment. Social workers are still dependent on the resident for collaborative information, however.

This reveals that, for the performance of their casework function, social workers are very much dependent on the resident. The nature of their complaints, however, is associated with the extent of the resident's autonomy. On the inpatient service where the resident decides whether a case needs social service, as well as the kind of service required (e.g., casework or financial assistance), social workers complain that residents do not send them casework referrals; they also complain that residents only refer cases requiring financial assistance. No social worker on the child service expresses either of these complaints. On the other hand, both inpatient and child social workers complain that residents do not collaborate with them.

According to the social workers, there are three general reasons for these difficulties, all of which, they state, stem from residents' being new to psychiatry. One is the residents' countertransference with the patient, so that "their identification with the patient is so strong they are hostile to other members of the family." Next, because the residents are learning, they are "anxious," "insecure," "defensive," and "threatened" by the social worker; also, female social workers are considered "threatening mother figures" to them. Finally, being new to psychiatry, residents do not know anything about the functions of social workers and fail to see the importance of family interaction and family dynamics; consequently, they do not think social work is very important or that it has much to offer. In other words, the residents' failure to co-operate is seen to derive from personal attributes of the individual—i.e., "insecurity" and a lack of knowledge. Consistent with the view that these difficulties stem mainly from the residents' being new to psychiatry is the claim that first-year residents are more difficult to work with than more experienced second and third-year residents.

The above assertions do not explain, however, why child psychiatric social workers express difficulty obtaining collaborative information but no difficulty obtaining referrals. Therefore, at least equally important is a structural factor: on the child service case referrals are routine procedure, whereas inpatient referrals depend on the residents' judgment concerning the needs of each case. Even if the inpatient social worker thinks the case needs social service, the resident may disagree; or he may decide to see the relative himself. The *standard procedure* of having someone see the patient's relative on the child service is, then, a structural mechanism obligating residents to perform activities that are complementary to the social worker's casework role. Less difficulty is encountered where it is "assumed" that the social worker will work with the relative, where the social workers' casework position "is more firmly established." Social workers experience less difficulty performing their casework role in child psychiatry, at least in part, because organizational rules (SOP) usually require casework services for each case. There is no such standard definition for the inpatient service.

Basically, most complaints about residents refer to their failure to initiate contact with social workers. On the inpatient service, if social workers want to perform casework, they must not wait until residents refer cases to them; for as one says, they "might just keep waiting." This is not to say that inpatient social workers claim that they never receive casework referrals. "If I did nothing, there would be some knocking on my door; but it facilitates matters if I knock on their door." Similarly with the child social workers, one of whom comments: "It's the social worker who usually takes more responsibility for these [collaborative] contacts."

It is in terms of the above considerations that the request for a specification of psychiatrists' "expectations" of social work should be considered. This request is a power strategy, the precise nature of which can be understood only after we have described activities social workers must perform to get case referrals and collaborative information. These activities are classified as implementing strategies.

IMPLEMENTING POWER STRATEGIES

Tertius Gaudens

As with the recreator, social workers find the residents' superior an important medium of influence. Social workers go to senior psychiatrists to influence residents' referral of casework cases, as well as to elicit collaborative information. For example:

> Another thing I do is call for a conference with the supervising psychiatrist. I can say that something about the case is bothering me. I'll bring up what I want to know and ask the psychiatrist for his opinion. He will have to ask the resident, and that way I'll find out.

The social worker cannot make the resident tell her what she wants to know, but she can initiate a situation in which he must tell his superior *in her presence.*

Initiating Positive Sanctions from Superiors

One social worker claims that since social workers are "ancillary," they cannot make residents see the importance of social work. "It has to come from higher up."

> Take ward rounds, for instance. Just the other day a case came up that I was working on. I knew something about the case, but didn't say anything. The chief resident asked me about it, and then I told what I knew. I told the chief resident.

This worker further states that if she had not waited until the chief resident recognized her as having something to contribute to the case, "the residents wouldn't have listened. They would have thought I was just talking about something I didn't know anything about." In this way, the social worker tries to get the importance of social work sanctioned by a source from "higher up"—the chief resident.

Defining One's Role in Terms of the Other's Self Interest

If a resident refuses to refer cases to an inpatient social worker, the latter may, on the basis of information obtained during ward rounds and from the patient's chart, see "an area where [she] can contribute to a case." She then approaches the resident and attempts to get him to initiate the referral.

> I try to get him to see the need to have a social worker on the case, but [let him think] it's his idea. Then he isn't threatened and is more accepting. I do it indirectly.

Upon being asked how this was done, the respondent replied that there were two approaches—the "theoretical" and the "specific."

In the "theoretical approach," she points out how social service might be of some general help to a particular type of patient. In the case of alcoholics and delinquency, for instance, there is often some situational factor involved in the patient's illness. The patient's wife may have a lot to do with why one is an alcoholic. "I will try to get them to see that if the spouse were helped with his or her feelings, some accompanying change might take place with the patients." The objective is to "try to get him to see that by working with the family I might help him attain his objective with the patient and give him greater understanding of the patient."

In the "specific approach," the worker will note specific things about the case from the patient's chart or from what has been said in ward rounds. For example, it might be noted that the patient's spouse has lost his job, "so I will say that it looks like the patient's husband needs some support while his wife is undergoing therapy." The respondent says that this approach usually works, but for some "I have to beat my head against a wall to get them to see the need for social work and treating the family."

"Catching on the run"

One way to obtain collaborative information is to stop the resident in the hall and ask him questions about the case. At first thought, one might be reluctant to classify such a simple phenomenon as an attempt to influence. It should be noted, however, that the social worker utilizes it to get facilities (information) from a resident who otherwise fails to volunteer this information by scheduling conferences with her. For example, for one such resident:

> I catch him in the hall, something like that—doing it on the run. He won't schedule conferences, so I just catch him on the run

like that. This has worked out okay; he seems to accept this; he tells me what I want to know.

Using "tact"

Finally, one inpatient social worker states that residents will often make referrals if they are directly approached "with a little tact." Care must be taken not to leave the impression that one is trying to infringe on the residents' treatment prerogative.

> From my observations and from what I hear in rounds, I might decide that the case needed a social worker. I would go to the therapist and suggest that some environmental thing might need looking into. Something like the family condition or welfare. They can usually accept this. It's the area of treatment that is threatening to them.

Note that the use of "tact" is seen in reference to the role responsibilities of the psychiatric resident and the social worker. The social worker is careful not to let the resident think that she is "treating" the relative. In other words, she observes and complies with certain status prerogatives of the resident.

There are several characteristics of the above strategies that should be noted. First, it is clear that they are attempts to influence the resident. Second, they represent a pattern of behavior since all eight social workers employ one or more of the strategies. It would be incorrect to infer from this, however, that corresponding to this pattern is a norm *prescribing* social workers to act in the above ways. Third, although all are influence attempts, none suggests that the resident's authority is being challenged; in their attempts to influence him, social workers do not tell the resident that a case needs social service. These strategies are, therefore, *oriented* to the structure of the social worker-resident relationship. Finally, they would not be so necessary if residents provided social workers with casework referrals and collaborative information more frequently; they are, then, costly activities. These last two characteristics will be discussed in greater detail.

Implementing Strategies as Oriented to a Normative Order

Although these strategies are goal oriented in that they are aimed at gaining access to patients' families and information about patients, they cannot be adequately understood solely in these terms. Neither are they behaviors which are strictly role behavior in conformity with a normative role structure. They are more correctly interpreted as reactions to the residents' failure to comply with needed facilities, but actions that are also oriented to the normative order—the residents' authority. Once the social workers' views of the residents' competence have been reviewed, the normative orientation of the influence attempts become clear.

In addition to their statements that residents lack knowledge about social work, and, therefore, fail to see its importance, social workers claim that residents know little about psychiatry and psychiatric skills. More than that, some feel that they are more knowledgeable than residents in the area of psychiatric treatment.

> I know more about interviewing and how to handle people's feelings than the resident does. . . . He hasn't had the training in how to handle people's feelings that we have had.

> Psychiatrists don't like to hear it, but it's a fact that social workers know more than the residents. The social worker is much more experienced and has more training than the resident.

On first consideration, these statements suggest that social workers do not legitimate the resident's authority. The suggestion is stronger in the following comments.

> He's the learner, but still he's the captain. Theoretically the social worker looks to the resident for professional guidance. But here he is occupying a position based on knowledge which he doesn't have. He is put in a position to direct and guide her, but he doesn't know as much in certain areas as she does.

> I have more knowledge and experience in psychiatry than they do when they first come here. They are placed in an authority position, but don't have the knowledge that goes along with it.

In the sense that social workers think they know more than the resident, they do not legitimate his superiority. They have not internalized the medical authority structure which implies that the doctor has superior knowledge vis-à-vis the "ancillary" profession. The "ancillary" here thinks he is more knowledgeable and competent than the superior regarding the superior's own skills.

An examination of the implementing strategies indicates, however, that certain "precautions" are taken not to invert the status order, that is, not to invalidate the resident's superiority. For example, social workers, thinking they know more than the resident, *could* inform him when he was doing something "wrong," such as his failure to refer cases to social workers when the latter thinks these services are needed. But no social worker indicates that this is done. As one states: "If he doesn't recognize it, I can't make him. If he won't see the need for a social worker on a certain case, I can't tell him what to do." One may "see an area where [social service] could contribute to the case," but "I don't usually go and say, 'Don't you want me to see Mrs. Jones.' I can do this, but I don't like to and usually don't." Instead, this respondent does it indirectly—using the "theoretical" and "specific" approaches to get residents "to see the need" and to initiate the referral. Consequently, residents are not "threatened." And, one might add, the superordinate-subordinate nature of the relationship is preserved.

Thus, although the residents' superiority is not *internally accepted,* it does elicit *overt compliance.* One may know more than residents, or at least think he does, but one cannot make it apparent. One must be "tactful" when working with residents.

> We have experience and training and contribute something to their training, but we have to do it tactfully. You have to make your contribution tactfully, almost inadvertently, yes, almost inadvertently. If some social worker has narcissistic needs, she can create a lot of problems. . . . If she has narcissistic needs, needs for status and recognition, if she wants a lot of attention she can cause a lot of trouble. We had a social worker here sometime back—she's not here any more. She had narcissistic needs: she wanted prestige and status and attention; she tried to show off what she knew to the residents. She tried to tell them how they were supposed to use social work. This rubbed the residents the wrong way. You can't let them think you know more than they do—this is heresy. Social workers are experienced and know more about certain aspects than residents, especially the new resident. But you can't let them know this. Although she may have known more than they did—she undoubtedly did, she had been here longer and knew her way around better, she was more experienced than they were—but you can't have these narcissistic needs and make the residents think you know more than they do and make them feel inferior.

Finally, an inpatient social worker indicates what may happen when the status order is inverted on an overt level. This worker was taken off a case because, she felt, the resident thought she was doing a "better job" with the relative than the resident was doing with the patient. She "had a very intense relationship with the relative," and in conference with the resident, "brought out all the information" that she had obtained. "Then the resident took me off the case." Although the social worker "didn't like it" and felt that the relative should continue seeing her, she could do nothing about it—"I couldn't contradict the resident." She also felt that the resident was "threatened" by her progress with the case, "felt that he had lost the race, that I had beat him and he couldn't take it." Whether this is the actual reason for the resident's taking the social worker off the case is not known. It, nevertheless, underscores the point that even when social workers may think they know more than residents (e.g., the case still required social service), the overt manifestation of their thoughts must be inhibited (e.g., the social worker had to terminate seeing the relative because she "couldn't contradict the resident").

Implementing Strategies as Costly Activity

Social workers sometimes volunteer the information that the above strategies "work." That is, they are rewarding because they get social workers something they value—case referrals, collaborative information. They are also the "extra efforts" necessitated by the residents' failure to co-operate. Therefore, to the extent that social workers do not like to perform them, or think that they should not have to, they are costs. Costs are involved because values are forgone—time, effort, and unpleasantness which accompany their performance. The following comments about the need to influence residents throw light on their costly nature. "I don't like to have to go asking them (residents). As a social worker, I think I have something to offer and it should be recognized." One states that she does not like the "bother" and "trouble" involved in having to "chase them down." For another it is "awkward" and "uncomfortable trying to get them to call us in." The "extra efforts" are not only oriented to the normative role structure of medical-"ancillary" authority relationships; they are also costly.

Understandably, social workers would like them eliminated. It is from this perspective that three additional strategies are to be considered, one of which is the appeal for expectations.

STRUCTURAL POWER STRATEGIES

Attempt to Evoke a Norm

Except for case referral on the child service, social workers are dependent on the residents' judgment concerning the patients' need for social service, and on both services for collaborative information. Because of the residents' autonomy, social workers have only limited normative (i.e., SOP) control over their behavior. In addition, social workers are "ancillary" and so are further limited in their control of residents—they cannot "tell" residents what to do.

The medical-"ancillary" authority structure is a rigid one and not subject to change.[7] However, the network of normative rules can be changed—within limits, of course: organizational rules and SOP's can be modified, eliminated, or added. The appeal for expectations is an attempt to add a rule.

Social workers were not asking for expectations per se, but for a particular kind of expectation. Remember their complaint that residents think they are useful only for financial assistance to patients, whereas their emphasis lies in the role of collaborator —someone who discusses with residents "family interaction and dynamics" and the bearing of these on the patient's illness. During the committee meetings, psychiatrists maintained that the social workers' duties consisted of "welfare" and work with "destitute families." Social workers collectively rejected this in favor of a role which "concerned [itself] with the pathology of the family and how it bears on the patient." Thus, they were not requesting psychiatrists to specify any kind of "expectation" of them. They were requesting that psychiatrists tell them they were expected to do casework treatment. *This is also the area in which they experienced difficulty working with residents.*

Role definitions are complementary in nature: expectations of persons performing one role are the obligations of persons performing other roles. Therefore, for psychiatrists, as the adminis-

7. See Harvey L. Smith, "Sociological Study of Hospitals" (unpublished Ph.D. dissertation, University of Chicago, 1949).

trators of the organization, to accept the social workers' request would place an obligation on the residents. Residents would be required to refer cases to social workers and to collaborate with them. Their decisions would become a matter of organizational rule and not just a matter of their individual judgment.

In sum, social workers felt a need to have their relationship with residents normatively prescribed. If psychiatrists had specified expectations of social workers consistent with the latter's definition of their role, they would have placed this relationship on a normative basis. The social workers' need is understandable in light of their dependence on the residents, who, they felt, did not always realize the "importance" of social workers, who failed to co-operate with them, and over whom they had little control. Therefore, social workers needed a more routine, stable, and reliable relationship with residents. At least one social worker sees the need for explicit expectations in terms of the social worker's dependency: "clarity of roles" is necessary because social workers have "to be so close to psychiatry" in the performance of their casework role.

> There are so many points where social work and psychiatry work together that there needs to be clarity of their roles.

Attempt at Coalition with Staff Psychiatrists

Coalitions exist when one party to a relationship uses its power against a third party in the interest of the second party of the relationship. Two illustrations will be given where the social workers attempted to form coalitions with staff psychiatrists in order to control the residents' behavior.

Direct Appeal: During the committee meetings, outright pleas were made for psychiatrists to utilize their authority to make residents co-operate with social workers. During one such request, the psychiatrists replied that social workers would have to "prove" they could make a contribution first; then residents would work with them. The social workers replied, "That's not true; the senior staff will have to make them work with us." The psychiatrists countered, "Prove you are worthy, prove you have something to contribute"; then, they said, residents would work with them.

Appeal for a Social Work-Staff Psychiatrist Administrative Committee: Excepting the supervisor, all social workers expressed a need for a permanent committee of psychiatrists to whom they could take their "problems," who would then communicate them to other psychiatrists. Psychiatrists saw no need for this committee and wanted to know why social workers should need it when the only other "ancillary" group (psychology) working on all three services did not. A social worker answered:

> We want to integrate with the team, the psychologists don't. They don't care what the psychiatrist does with their test results. They give him their results, and they don't care what he does with them. We have to be closer. What we do is more dependent on the psychiatrist.

This, of course, does not say that social workers were attempting to form a coalition. It does indicate, however, that at least one social worker sees the need for the committee to derive from the social workers' dependence on psychiatrists (residents) in the performance of their casework role.

A subsequent interview statement from a social worker lends more explicit support to the interpretation that this was an attempt at coalition formation.[8]

> [The committee would be useful because] the people [psychiatrists] on the committee would have a broader understanding of the functions of social work, and in their supervision and teaching of medical students and residents a more constructive view of social work could be given. The psychiatrists could communicate this to other psychiatrists too. It would be a spreading of the knowledge, so to speak.

Or, one may say, it would be spreading the social workers' definition of their role by persons who have the power to get it accepted. It is an attempt by the social workers to project their definition of the situation into the organization, that is, to facilitate the institutionalization of their definition of the social work role.

These strategies are similar to the implementing strategies in that they attempt to influence the residents' role performance.

8. For an additional analysis of potential functions of the proposed committee, see below, pp. 180-81.

They have an additional trait in common with certain of the previous strategies (e.g., *tertius gaudens*). They indicate a medical "ancillary" group's need to gain access to a greater source of authority to accomplish something—in this case, the acceptance or institutionalization of the "ancillary" group's definition of their role. Being "ancillary" and working with junior psychiatrists who have authority over them, they are unable to do this themselves. Therefore, they appeal to a level above the junior psychiatrists.

One social worker speaks of the problem in the following way. Feeling the need for a well-defined conception of the social workers' role, she has tried to obtain a "clear-cut statement" from psychiatrists "about what they wanted from social work," but has failed to do so. She realizes that social workers themselves "could formulate a plan, but the mechanics" would not be there to make it work. Only when it comes from an administrator with "sufficient authority" in the Department to get it accepted will the "mechanics" be there. "It [will] have to come administratively. Then the mechanics will be there."

The structural strategies are clearly different from the implementing strategies in two major aspects. First, they are directed toward bringing about a structural change or modification in the Department whereas the other strategies are not: (A) They would have created new relationships in the form of a committee to whom social workers could take their "problems." (B) They would have modified existing relationships through senior psychiatrists utilizing their authority over residents ("direct appeal" for coalition formation), and by prescribing an explicit definition of the social work role consistent with the social workers' own definition, thereby modifying the social worker-resident relationship. They are, therefore, structural strategies.

Second, if they had been effective, it is inferred that the need for implementing strategies would have been eliminated, at least in part. Thus, they are classified as cost-reducing strategies. Since none of these strategies were accepted and put into effect by psychiatrists, their effectiveness as cost-reducing structural mechanisms cannot be evaluated. Conclusions in this regard must rest on tenuous mental experimentation—thinking what would have been their effect had they been accepted. Nevertheless, a few months after the study began, a structural change occurred in the admissions procedure on the inpatient service which lends validity to this interpretation.

STRUCTURAL CHANGE IN THE INPATIENT ADMISSIONS PROCEDURE

Prior to the change in inpatient admissions procedure, social workers rarely had contact with the patient and his family.[9] The new procedure changed this.

Under the old system, no one accompanied the patient and his relative from the psychiatric admissions office to the hospital general finance and admissions offices back to the Department and to his assigned ward. Consequently, patients sometimes got lost. In addition, patients referred to the hospital by private physicians were often classified as private patients, although they had insufficient income to pay private patient fees. The head of the inpatient service felt that these problems could be eliminated if social workers interviewed the patient and the accompanying relative upon arrival. Also, because of their training and skill in interviewing techniques, social workers could greet patients "in a more effective way" and establish greater rapport with them than could the admissions officer who was not a trained interviewer.

Under the new system, one day prior to a patient's admission, the inpatient admissions officer informs the social service secretary of the patient's scheduled arrival. One inpatient social worker is on admissions duty each day and will reserve this time in her schedule. When the patient arrives, the admissions officer informs the social worker, who then escorts the patient through the admissions procedure. First, however, the social worker has a joint interview with the patient and his family.

The new procedure is of most value to the social worker because of this interview. At this time, appointments to see the relative(s) may be arranged, provided the patient is to be admitted to the admission social worker's ward. If the patient is assigned to another ward, the interviewer gives the relative the name and sometimes the phone number of the social worker who works on that ward. The possibility of the ward social worker's sending an appointment letter to the family may be mentioned. The family is also advised that it can arrange appointments

9. See above, pp. 65-66.

with a social worker through the social service secretary. In this interview, then, the social worker makes contact with the patient's relatives without going through the resident, schedules appointments with them, and informs them of the services provided by social workers in case they later decide to utilize social service.

Regarding referrals, a major change is obviously created in the inpatient social worker-resident relationship. The new structure reduces the social worker's dependency on the resident for referrals, thereby structuring *out* much of his power over her. All inpatient social workers express approval of this change and agree that it is easier to get "referrals." [10]

> It makes things easier for referrals. Under the old setup you had to go to the resident or wait until he came to you. If you had a resident who thinks he's God and knows everything, and you say that you have talked with the patient's husband and that you think you should see Mr. Jones, he might say, no, I'll talk to Mr. Jones myself. There's nothing you can do when a resident is like that. This way [the new procedure] you aren't as likely to be pushed around. If you think the case needs social service, you can go on and make arrangements to see the relative. It makes it a little more operating procedure for giving you more freedom to use your own professional judgment and to go on and do what your professional knowledge indicates needs to be done. It's not going behind the resident's back; it's standard operating procedure.

One says referral is easier because "It's automatic—because we don't have to wait for the resident to refer the cases. With the new admissions setup we are already there and don't have to wait." Another states that while "the resident is still the final authority—he's still captain of the team—we have a little more freedom in what we do. . . . Whereas, under the old setup we had to be asked to come in on a case," with the new setup "I can move right in."

In brief, the new procedure allows the social workers' enactment of their (self-defined) role without being hindered as much by residents. Or, as one put it, "It made for the social worker's role being defined administratively rather than dependent on the resident." Thus, a structural change initiated by the head of

10. Technically speaking, when the social worker obtains a case through her direct contact with the patient and his family, it is not a referral in the true sense of the word, for the doctor has not referred the case to her.

the inpatient staff did what the social worker's structural power strategies did not do. Still, there is some evidence that the change was actually initiated by the social workers themselves. For example, one of the social workers stated,

it was up to _____ [head of inpatient service] to initiate it. Social work, historically, has been involved in admissions procedure. They have now recognized this, but before we weren't involved in admissions nearly so much. . . . But it was up to [head of inpatient service] to initiate it. We couldn't have done it without his okay. So it was his green light that initiated it. . . . But this is not altogether true. _____ has been here a long time and laid the ground work with him. Over the years she had been putting the bug in his ear that social workers needed to be in on admissions. So finally he comes around, but, of course, he thinks it's his idea. It has to be that way, you know. [Smiles.] It's got to be his idea.

In any case, structural changes in the admissions procedure give social workers greater freedom to use their own "professional judgment." This is due to the peculiarities of the power dynamics involved in the relationships between the two professional groups. Under the previous setup,

if [the resident] didn't want a social worker in on a case, he could prevent it. If he was insecure or anxious, he might refuse to call a social worker in. Now we can be in on the case from the very beginning. He may [still] not see the need for anyone seeing the family. . . . But now we aren't nearly so dependent on him [to call us in].

To be consistent with our previous analysis, the structural change should result in a reduction of costly implementing strategies which were present under the former structure. Indeed, the cost-cutting function of the new structure is very clearly revealed in the following comparison of the two structures. The social worker who had said it was "uncomfortable trying to get [residents] to call us in," states that under the old procedure it was often necessary to

go to the resident if I thought a case needed social service. I would have to go to him and say that I've been looking at the chart and that it looks like the case could use social service. Then I would have to . . . try to get him to see the need. This

makes for an awkward situation. Now this is not necessary—
I can get on the case from the beginning.

By structuring out the residents' power, the new procedure structured out costly implementing strategies.

These cost-cutting consequences are in great part unintended
and unanticipated consequences—latent functions[11]—of the
change. The change was initiated by the head of the inpatient
service to prevent patients from getting lost, to make sure they
had accurate information about the costs of hospitalization, and
to have patients "greeted in a more effective way" and "put at
ease" by trained persons. There is no indication that an *intended*
consequence was to remove the social workers from the power
of the resident, to make the referral system easier for social workers, nor to eliminate their costly activities. To be sure, strains in
social relationships precipitated the change, but the strains were
in the patient-department relationship and not the resident-social
worker relationship. Nevertheless, the change resulted in a reduction of strain in the latter (at least from the social workers'
viewpoint).

SUMMARY AND CONCLUSIONS

Social workers and psychiatrists indicate a lack of consensus
regarding the definition of the social workers' role. The social
workers argue that their role is one of collaborative treatment
with families; psychiatrists argue that it consists of welfare services. The analysis of the social workers' reactions to residents'
failure to co-operate with them in the collaborative casework
role further demonstrates the empirical relevance of the power
strategy concept. Data show quite clearly how this concept refers
to behaviors that are *oriented to,* rather than in *conformity with,*
an institutionalized social structure—in the present case, the
medical-"ancillary" authority structure. Also, consistent with the
analysis of the recreator, two distinct types of power strategies—
implementing and structural—are derived. Implementing strategies are less efficient than structural strategies because they
require extra individual effort, are "uncomfortable" and "awkward." Although they are necessary for the social workers' performance of their instrumental casework role, they are neverthe-

11. Robert K. Merton, *Social Theory and Social Structure* (rev. and enlr. ed.;
Glencoe: The Free Press, 1957), p. 51.

less cost-inducing. Data reveal that the distinction between implementing and structural strategies is not only useful in terms of the initial process of institutionalization and of becoming established, but also in making a conceptual distinction in the on-going social process which takes place within more established social structures.

Differences in the structure of referrals between the inpatient and child services reveal that differential referral procedures are related to differences in complaints about residents. Also, the structural change on the inpatient service provided additional insight into the problem of how a normative order—in this case, a change in the normative structure of referrals—can eliminate the need for cost-inducing implementing strategies. These findings, therefore, are consistent with the conclusions based on the study of the recreation service regarding the cost-cutting function of normative rules (organizational SOP's). We now turn to an explicit test of this hypothesis.

6 CLINICAL PSYCHOLOGY:
SOCIAL STRUCTURE AND
THE CONCEPT OF COST

The previous two chapters have focused on power strategies, outlining certain of their relationships to institutionalized rules. It was *inferred* that rules which regulate alter's behavior —his use of facilities—reduce ego's costs. However, since the strategy of invoking rules was not successful for either the recreator or social workers, the validity of this hypothesis was not demonstrated. Consequently, conclusions are largely based on mental experiment; they are based on what we can reasonably assume would have happened if these strategies had been successful and norms introduced. In the first part of this chapter, analysis of a relationship characterized by explicit rules provides a more conclusive test for the hypothesis. In the second part, additional problems of rules are considered, along with actors' reactions to structurally depriving conditions. Data are based on a study of clinical psychologists.

In the Department there are ten full-time psychologists, including a chief supervisor, and three part-time psychologists who are also working on graduate degrees. Eight of the full-time members have a Ph.D., and the other two are currently working toward theirs.

Psychologists perform four different roles in the Department. All except two spend a major portion of their time performing a diagnostic testing role. The two exceptions are hired primarily for research, although others also perform research functions. Ten treat patients, and seven of the Ph.D.'s perform a teaching role. Teaching functions are performed in both the university Department of Psychology and the School of Medicine. Psychologists teach residents, medical students, and nurses, as well as students on the campus. They also supervise graduate students from the Department of Psychology who are doing their clinical psychology internship in the Department of Psychiatry. Those involved in teaching functions hold a joint appointment in the university Department of Psychology and in the Department of Psychiatry. The major appointment is in the Department of Psychiatry, however.

An obvious difference between psychologists on the one hand and the recreator and social workers on the other is the former's performance of several roles—teaching, diagnosis, psychotherapy, and research. Still, the primary role is the administration of diagnostic tests; eleven of the thirteen are hired primarily to perform the diagnostic testing role. As the psychology supervisor expresses it, "This is the first priority of the Psychiatry Department." It is in this role that psychologists are most comparable to the recreator and social workers: its performance depends upon case referral from residents. Accordingly, it is in terms of this role that the cost-cutting hypothesis will be tested. Other roles will be considered from somewhat different, but related, perspectives.

THE PSYCHOLOGIST'S DIAGNOSTIC ROLE: TESTING A HYPOTHESIS

The diagnostic role involves three sets of activities: (1) administration of psychological tests to patients; (2) a verbal report of the test results during ward rounds on the inpatient service and diagnostic conferences on the outpatient and child services; and (3) a written report, which is entered in the patient's chart. With few exceptions tests are administered to residents' patients, although ward rounds and diagnostic conferences are supervised by staff psychiatrists.

Diagnostic tests are of two types: routine tests and battery tests. The routine tests are the Minnesota Multiphasic Personality Inventory (MMPI) and sentence completion tests, and are routinely given to patients upon admission. Battery tests require specific referrals: the physician requests specific information (e.g., Is the patient psychotic? Is there evidence for brain damage?). The psychologist then selects from his battery the test(s) he considers appropriate to deal with the problem.

STRUCTURE OF REFERRALS: THE FUNCTION
OF INSTITUTIONALIZED RULES

Because of the structure of the psychologist-resident relationship, psychologists experience few difficulties working with residents in the area of diagnosis. In contrast to recreation and social work referrals, which are face-to-face and depend upon the residents' judgment, routine psychological test referrals do not depend upon the resident's judgment, nor do they involve face-to-face contact. There are exceptions to this for battery testing. Routine tests are discussed first.

On two of the inpatient wards, all patients are given the MMPI and sentence completion tests. When a patient is admitted, the ward secretary informs the ward psychologist, who contacts the patient and administers the test. He then writes his report and gives it to the ward secretary, who enters it in the patient's chart. Consequently, psychologist and resident have little direct contact in referral procedure.

> Everything goes through the secretary. I don't have any contact with the resident. It's a mechanical thing with these routine tests.

Two things are to be noted. First, contacts between resident and psychologist are structured out of the referral procedure, so there is little opportunity for difficulties between them. The secretary mediates between them in a double sense. She informs the psychologist when patients are ready for testing, and she relays his report to the resident by putting it in the patient's chart. This eliminates psychologist-resident contact.

> Sometimes I [psychologist] will call the resident and let him know what the test results indicate if there's something I think is important. But other than this there isn't much contact. Most everything goes through the ward secretary.

Second, all patients are "mechanically" given the two tests; it is an organizational rule that all patients on the two wards be given these tests. Consequently, diagnostic testing by the psychologist is *not* dependent on the resident's judgment as to whether his patient should be tested. Accordingly, psychologists have no complaint about receiving referrals. The costs of influencing residents to make referrals, and in chasing them down, are eliminated; they are structured out by the presence of the formal "referral" procedure.[1] A *different* referral procedure used on the third ward further documents this conclusion.

On this ward, residents must fill out a referral form indicating the patient's testability[2] and put it in the patient's chart. The psychologist then obtains the referral form from the ward secretary. Here, again, the ward secretary mediates the psychologist-resident relationship; but the referral and subsequent test administration depends on the residents' decision. Whereas psychologists on the other two wards indicate no difficulties in MMPI and sentence completion test referrals, psychologists on this ward do.

> The routine testing is somewhat different [on my ward], since the resident indicates whether the patient is testable or not. The more disturbed patients are sent to our ward and some of the patients are not testable. The resident sometimes forgets to indicate this in the chart, so I often have to chase him down and find out if he wants the patient tested. [This is done] informally. I will see him and ask him if he wants a particular patient tested.

The costs of "chasing the resident down" are not as completely structured out of the referral procedure on this ward as on the other two wards.

On the outpatient service all patients are also given the two routine tests. The resident interviews the patient and then takes a referral form to the psychologists' secretary. The secretary informs the psychologist that the patient is ready to be tested. The procedure here is also "routine" and "automatic," where "every-

1. In light of data to be introduced later in this chapter, which reveal that several psychologists dislike the diagnostic function, it might be that at least some psychologists would never try to influence residents to make diagnostic referrals in the event that they fail to do so. Nevertheless, this structural feature has the above effect to the extent that psychologists are motivated, or otherwise feel the responsibility, to give diagnostic tests to patients if residents fail to refer patients to them.
2. The ward in question houses the more seriously disturbed patients, some of whom are not testable.

thing goes through the secretaries," so that contact with the resident is only "tangential."

> The referral is routine. The [outpatient service] secretary assigns the patient to the resident and gives him the patient's chart. After he has interviewed him, he knows to send him for tests. This usually runs smoothly; there aren't any problems.

With the exception of the one inpatient ward, then, no psychologist on the outpatient or inpatient services experiences difficulty with residents regarding referrals for MMPI and sentence completion tests. This attests to the general importance of the two structural mechanisms—organizational rules (routine testing of all patients) and secretaries—in eliminating costly activity for psychologists. Residents are prevented from interfering with the psychologists' role performance. As one psychologist states while discussing the "mechanical" nature of referrals, "he [resident] can't mess up what we do." A resident, in commenting on testing referrals, states: "It's all routine. He [psychologist] knows when he should give the psychologicals. I don't have any contact with him really." Consequently, costly activities (e.g., "chasing the resident down") are prevented because the rule specifies that each patient shall be tested. Everything operates according to prescribed rules.

On both services, however, difficulties are encountered in referrals for battery testing. Inpatient battery referrals are much like routine ones because referral forms go through the ward secretary. An important difference is that residents individually initiate battery referrals. Consequently, "Occasionally a resident can be a pain in the neck for battery testing." Psychologists complain that referrals are vague and unspecific, or a lack of rationale is given for them. For example, the referral may only ask for "dynamics." An inpatient psychologist states:

> The only criticism I have in terms of referrals would be the residents' not asking specific questions. Vague questions and referrals do not facilitate doing my job any. When this happens, I have to go to them to ask them what they mean.

Other psychologists who work (or have worked) on the inpatient service also mention the necessity to "chase the resident down" when he fails to specify why he wants battery testing. At least one incurs the cost of "discomfort" when he must ask residents why they want battery testing.

When I first came on the service, the residents had just come on too, so I got to know them and they got to know me. We were all new and I established good relationships with them. Whenever they would give me a vague referral, I would go to them and ask them what they wanted me to try to find out. With others that I didn't have such a good relationship, I would do the same thing, but I wouldn't be comfortable.

Finally, inpatient psychologists complain about the resident who tries to tell them the kind of test to use. For example:

The referral he gives me might read, use the Rorschach. I don't like this. I don't want him telling me what test to use. I know my tests and which ones I need to use. All I want him to do is just tell me what he wants to know, and I'll select the test.

Thus, differential degrees of routinization result in different degrees of costs to the psychologists. Because battery test referrals are not as routinized as other referrals, costs are not as completely structured out of the referral procedure. It is true that battery referrals are routinized—all are by written request and go through the secretaries, but their specific nature is not. The appropriate test used depends upon a specific communication from the resident, which depends upon the resident's problem with the patient. When this communication is vague and unclear, the psychologist incurs the cost of time and energy (and discomfort) "chasing the resident down" to ascertain the reason for referral and, therefore, the appropriate test(s) to use.

In the outpatient clinic a few battery tests are given to private patients who are referred by staff psychiatrists and other hospital physicians, but they are rarely used. Aside from battery referrals sometimes being sent on too short notice, no complaints are voiced.

On the child psychiatric service, all testing is of the battery variety. Like referrals on the other two services, there is little contact between psychologist and resident because referrals go through secretaries. Unlike the other services, however, all testing is in reference to a specific problem. Accordingly, the resident must decide what he specifically wants the psychologist to find out about the patient. Consequently, the psychologist will not want a "vague" referral:

> Psychologist: We have the trouble of their knowing, or not knowing, what we can find out. Sometimes their referrals are next to useless. They might say they want a complete personality evaluation. This doesn't say anything. All we know to go on here is that it only tells you that personality tests are needed and not intelligence tests. It's much more useful if they tell us what's going on with the patient—what the problem seems to be.

> Interviewer: Your tests in child are not routine, like the MMPI and sentence completion on the inpatient service?

> Psychologist: No. The tests will vary with the child and what his problem is. We have a number of tests and we need to know something about the patient's background, what his parents think the problem is, in order to have something to go on. Although we have a lot of tests, we need to have some information about the case before we know what tests to give. They should ask specific questions about the patient—like, is the child psychotic? But some of the referrals are pretty vague.

> Interviewer: What do you do when you get a vague referral?

> Psychologist: I will look at the charts and see what's in them. The in-take interview with the parent will usually be in there and it may indicate what the parents think the trouble is. If the child has a language handicap, I can find it out. If the information is not available in the charts, then *I chase down the resident.*

Nevertheless, child service psychologists indicate that these problems are minimal since "administratively it's set up pretty good." Like the other services, all referrals go through secretaries rather than directly from resident to psychologist. "I have nothing to do with them [referrals]. They come through routine procedures. The secretary does the referral. She schedules them for me." Most complaints stem from the vague character of referrals; one psychologist also complains that residents occasionally refer cases on too short notice. Child service referrals are not as routinized as most referrals on the other services.

This description of the system of referrals for psychological testing reveals basic differences between testing referrals and recreation and social work referrals. Psychologists, in contrast to recreator and social workers, voice no problem of residents' failing to use their services, and express little difficulty in working with them. Two structural mechanisms account for this difference. One is the fact that the administration of psychological tests is highly routine. Unlike the case of inpatient social service, for example, the resident is given *no option* for referring patients for psychological testing, except in cases of battery testing. As a result, the resident can have little influence on the psychologist's role performance, no matter how little he may need testing service. For example, an outpatient resident, who feels that tests are valueless, must nevertheless make testing referrals.

> The patient is referred for two routine tests. These are the MMPI and sentence completion. The referral is a routine—I have no choice in this. This is the way it's done here—all patients have to be referred for these two tests.

Secretaries constitute a secondary structural mechanism protecting psychologists from the residents' power to interfere with their role performance. They mediate between the resident and psychologist so that there is little contact between the two in the referring procedure. This was not always the case, however. Formerly:

> Things got very chaotic, very complicated. The psychologist would be busy and someone would ask him to do a referral for him right away. He would be too busy and say so, and this was often taken as a personal affront.

With secretaries mediating the relationship, opportunities for such "personal affronts" are reduced. And when residents try to deviate from the formal procedure by verbally requesting a battery testing, psychologists request them to go through the prescribed procedure. For example, a psychologist, in commenting on residents who sometimes approach him directly, says: "I'll never do a battery unless there is a written referral; never a verbal referral."

This analysis of testing referrals provides additional support for the hypothesis that when normative rules are applied to alter's actions they reduce ego's costs. Although it is the resident's patient whom the psychologist tests, he can "do this fairly independently" of the resident because a set of organizational rules and procedures prescribes the resident's behavior (i.e., to refer or not to refer). At least one psychologist is aware of the function performed by this independence from the resident.

> It's funny. I don't know whether it was planned this way or not, but being independent of the resident like this I have an idea it prevents a lot of problems.

The potentially explosive situation where the Ph.D. psychologist finds himself taking a direct "order" from a member of another profession, a neophyte to that profession at that, does not occur.

In addition, the presence of secretaries contributes to the psychologist's independence and, therefore, to the reduction of his costs. Without rules routinizing the resident's actions, however, this feature is insufficient to eliminate all costs. For where the resident's behavior is not highly routinized—in battery test referrals and even "routine" test referrals on one ward—psychologists incur measures of costs not incurred in other situations.

In general, then, psychologists experience few difficulties obtaining facilities (referrals) in their diagnostic role performance. Unlike the recreator and social workers, they must rarely exert cost-inducing influence attempts to obtain referrals. Because the residents' activities have been institutionalized, most of the psychologist's costs have been structured out of the psychologist-resident relationship, permitting him autonomous role performance.

There is one additional structural feature which eliminates costs for the psychologist in his diagnostic role. After giving his report in diagnostic conferences or ward rounds, the psychologist terminates his relationship with the case.

> After my report is written and the results have been discussed, I feel my function is completed; the management of the patient is pretty much up to the physician.

> I don't have a continuing relationship with the residents. In rounds I will have some contact with them, and I may discuss the patient with them before I write up my report, but there's nothing in the way of a structured relationship. There's no need for scheduling appointments, nothing like that.

Thus, another structural factor accounting for the absence of difficulty between psychologist and resident is, then, the *absence of a continuing relationship* between them. Psychologists have nothing comparable to the social workers' casework relationship which requires continuing collaboration with residents. Consequently, the resident's treatment decision can have no effect on the psychologist's diagnostic role (which is the psychologist's major role in the Department).

> There is no need for a continuing relationship with the resident. After we've completed our diagnostics, we're through with the case. There is no team setup insofar as the resident's therapy with the patient is concerned. We have no interest in the case after the diagnosis has been made. We don't have any collaborative or continuing relationship with the resident at all. Our relationship is limited to the team in the diagnostic case conference. We are more independent [of the resident] than social work. Social workers are tied pretty closely to them. That's one reason social workers have more problems with them than we do. We have *no occasion to have difficulty with them, really.*

FURTHER CONSIDERATIONS
OF SOCIAL STRUCTURE
AND THE CONCEPT OF COST

To understand certain crucial problems psychologists face in hospitals, one must realize that psychologists are trained in an academic setting. In this setting emphasis is on teaching and research, and one has autonomy in what he teaches and selects for research. There is no image of an academic man with a routine work schedule, hired primarily for something other than research and teaching, where his work is important primarily for its service to another profession. Nevertheless, these are the conditions of the psychologist's work situation in the Department. To be sure, psychologists perform teaching and research functions, but the primary duty for most of them is aiding the psychiatrist in patient diagnosis.

In this section, the general hypothesis tested in the foregoing section will be further specified. Examination of the psychologist's other three roles will reveal that alter's *deviation* from formal rules may sometimes reduce ego's costs rather than induce them; also, rules protecting ego's autonomy and reducing his costs in one role may have a more general cost-inducing effect when their effect on *another role* is considered. Finally, the function of joint appointments in the departments of psychiatry and psychology will be evaluated.

The analysis of these three roles will revolve around the issue

of autonomy. Understandably, persons trained in academic settings will value autonomy. Psychologists, however, find themselves working for another profession—they are one of psychiatry's "ancillaries." In addition there is the general problem
of the professional working in a bureaucratic setting: The professional desires autonomy and independence but must, to a
certain extent, be controlled and regulated by formal routine
so that his activities will co-ordinate with others.

Data indicate that psychologists do incur the cost of a lack of
autonomy. Data also reveal that certain individual reactions and
structural mechanisms protect their autonomy. The primary problem in this section is, therefore, to understand where psychologists are permitted autonomy and where they are deprived of it
in teaching, psychotherapy, and research. In general, we want to
determine in what respects psychologists "are autonomous, but
subject to control," as one psychologist remarked.

PSYCHOTHERAPY: SUPERVISION WITH AUTONOMY

Ten of the thirteen psychologists perform psychotherapy. Except for one member who treats three patients, none carries more
than two patients at a time. Usually the patients are adults, although occasionally a psychologist in the child service treats a
child. In all cases, treatment is on an outpatient basis. Like the
residents, psychologists treat only staff patients and are supposed
to be supervised by senior psychiatrists.

Other than the actual treatment itself, there are two phases
involved in the performance of the treatment role: getting a
patient and obtaining supervision. Regarding the former, psychologists obtain patients in the same manner as do residents on
the outpatient and child services. Although patients are occasionally secured through the diagnostic conference, they are
usually selected from the residents' waiting list. Freedom to go
directly to the residents' waiting list and select the patient one
wishes undoubtedly performs an important function. It prevents
psychologists from having to receive "permission" from psychiatrists to treat patients. Therefore, their performance of psychotherapy does not depend on individual psychiatrists' opinion
of the psychologists' competence and right to conduct psychotherapy. Accordingly, no psychologist has any complaints about
obtaining patients. The situation could be explosive if the Ph.D.

psychologist had to obtain permission from a psychiatrist to treat patients, especially if the psychiatrist did not share the psychologist's opinion of the latter's competence and qualifications to conduct psychotherapy.

Also, with but three exceptions, psychologists express no dissatisfaction with the Department policy requiring them to have psychiatric supervision when they treat patients. The potential problem involved here is suggested by one of the three who is dissatisfied. The respondent says he does not like the policy simply because he does not like to be supervised. It is also disliked because "it's a matter of us having to go to them to ask them for something." Interestingly, this psychologist is leaving the organization to accept a faculty position. The reason given for leaving is a lack of "latitude in [his] time commitment"; that is, "not enough time to do research" and to teach. Perhaps, the strictures supervision places on his autonomy enter into his dislike for it. Further light on this problem is provided by another psychologist who also dislikes the policy.

> Some staff members [psychologists] have been seeing patients for as long as some of the staff psychiatrists, and I'm quite sure they are just as competent. This gives you a peculiar feeling— it's a bit irritating having to have a supervisor when you are experienced like some of them [psychologists] are. Because of the possibility of somatic illness, there should be a medical person that the psychologist can go to if he wants to do so and sees the need to do so, but I don't think it's right that members of our staff who are experienced in treating patients should have to have a supervisor. I feel it's a professional insult to psychologists who have had years of experience to have to have a staff psychiatrist supervise them.

Thus, to be deprived of autonomy and independence in treating patients is professionally insulting. Actually, the respondent expresses no dissatisfaction with the supervision itself: "I've only been seeing patients for two years and I need to learn a lot more before I can begin to think of doing therapy without supervision." Neither is there dissatisfaction with the respondent's particular supervisor. "Individually I have no complaints. I like my supervisor, Dr. —————, very much. *He doesn't try to supervise each session I have.* I see him once a week, and we discuss what I've been doing with each of my patients and he gives me suggestions that are very helpful." The respondent is not dissatisfied with the actual operation of supervision, but with the *formal* policy requiring him to have psychiatric supervision.

In light of their academic background which allows—in fact, encourages—independence and autonomy, it is understandable that subordination to members of another profession is costly to psychologists. However, the costs of this formal policy are reduced because of the way supervision is exerted, as is suggested by the above respondent. For example, one psychologist states that he is "supposed" to have psychiatric supervision, but this has not reduced his autonomy.

Psychologist: For some [psychiatrists] it's a matter of bookkeeping and just the record of having someone take medical responsibility. I've been lucky in getting people to work with. I haven't had any trouble at all with any of them.

Interviewer: You say you haven't had any trouble with the ones you have worked with. You mean there are some whom you might have trouble with if they were your supervisor?

Psychologist: Yes.

Interviewer: What would these persons do that would make it difficult for you to work with them?

Psychologist: It would depend on the attitude of the supervisor. Some will just see it as an administrative measure—just something that's done. But if he wanted to see it as a regular supervisory relationship, I wouldn't see the patient under those circumstances.

Interviewer: How do you feel about psychologists having to have psychiatrists as supervisors?

Psychologist: Well, as a general abstract principle I don't like this. On the other hand when you realize you are working in a medical setting, you have to accept this. If you don't like this, you should work somewhere else. I personally feel you need someone to talk over your case. Yet, if I were forced to work with someone I couldn't work with, someone who wanted to see it as a regular supervisory relationship, I wouldn't do it. But I haven't been bothered, really. The business of having to have someone as medical supervisor is really rather silly. By putting it that psychologists have to have psychiatrists as supervisors, it gets framed that we can't be trusted.

The two psychologists immediately above dislike the formal policy of supervision, but do not mind its actual operation: the formal policy which could restrict their autonomy is not exerted. Other psychologists distinguish between the "formal" and the "actual," although they do not dislike the formal because the actual operates as it does. For one, a policy of requiring psychiatric supervision "can be the height of ridiculousness if it's enforced rigidly." But it has not been enforced. He considers supervision as only "medical responsibility": he goes to the psychiatrist when *he* sees the need, rather than according to regularly scheduled meetings. There are circumstances in which the respondent desires close supervision, but he wants "the prerogative of determining this." He has this prerogative. Another respondent is even more explicit about not disliking the unenforced formal policy.

Interviewer: Do you have supervision when you treat patients?

Psychologist: Minimally. [Indicates that in one case there is fairly close contact with the psychiatrist because the latter is "fairly interested in the case." As a rule, however, there is little contact between the respondent and the psychiatrist-supervisor.]

Interviewer: Do you have a psychiatric supervisor on each case you treat?

Psychologist: *Technically* I do, but in *actual practice* I don't.

Interviewer: How do you mean, technically you do?

Psychologist: Technically there is a psychiatrist who is supervisor, but *I never see him.* I could go to him *if* I had a medical problem. I *could* go to him *if* a particular problem came up.

Interviewer: But, in a technical sense, you have to have a psychiatrist assigned to the case as the supervisor?

Psychologist: Yes.

Interviewer: How do you feel about having to have a psychiatrist as supervisor?

Psychologist: It doesn't bother me. I feel the need occasionally to go to psychiatrists for medical knowledge. *It doesn't bother me because it is used the way it is.*

Interviewer: How do you mean?

Psychologist: You can go to him *if you want to,* and if you don't, you don't have to. So far as actual practice is concerned I could be supervised by a psychologist if I wanted to.

Interviewer: You mean, while technically the psychiatrist is supervisor, you could actually work with a psychologist?

Psychologist: That's right.

Interviewer: But you don't mind the SOP that a psychiatrist is the supervisor?

Psychologist: It all depends on the psychiatrist. If he were a decent one, no. If he weren't, I would resent it very much.

Still others are not even aware of the formal policy. One states that psychologists can profit from going to psychiatrists—for "counseling consultation," especially regarding medical matters, but that psychologists are not required to have psychiatrists for supervisors. Two, who perform no psychotherapy, state they would not have to be supervised by psychiatrists if they did. Another recognizes that he is formally supposed to have psychiatric supervision, but he currently has a psychologist for his supervisor. The remaining three realize they must have psychiatric supervision to treat patients but are not opposed to the policy. They feel a need for supervision because of their inexperience, and prefer psychiatrists to psychologists as supervisors because of the formers' greater experience.

With the possible exception of the psychologist who is leaving the Department, there are no complaints about supervision operating to restrict the psychologist's autonomy. The above data, therefore, uncover an important difference between the psychologist's diagnostic role and his therapeutic role. In the former, formal procedures which bind the actions of another (the resident) enable the psychologist to operate autonomously. It is when deviations occur (e.g., vague referrals) that costs are induced and psychologists hindered in their task performance. For the therapeutic role, it is due to the fact that the other *does* deviate from formal rules that the psychologist attains autonomy and independence. The hypothesis that normative rules—when applied to alter's actions—function to reduce ego's costs must, then, be further specified. Rules which elicit alter's conformity cut costs for ego if they prescribe alter's actions that facilitate ego's task performance and goal attainment—in this case, autonomous role performance. But when the rules prescribe actions which prevent ego's attainment of desired values, alter's deviation is cost reducing.

RESEARCH: BUREAUCRACY AS INTRUDER ON AUTONOMY

In this section, concern will be with those psychologists for whom research is an important value. First, those who express no desire to do research will be eliminated.

Twelve psychologists were asked to rank, in terms of their preference, the following functions: research, teaching, diagnosis, and psychotherapy. One was unable to do so because he liked all four equally well. Three rated research last in preference, and one placed it next to last. Another placed it second but stated this was only temporary; as a general thing he does not prefer research to other functions. The rankings of the other six psychologists are presented in Table 1.

TABLE 1   RANK ORDER OF WORK PREFERENCES FOR PSYCHOLOGISTS WHO EXPRESS A PREFERENCE TO DO RESEARCH

Psychol- ogist	"A"[a]	"B"[a,b]	"C"	"D"	"E"	"F"
Rank Order	Research	Research	Teaching	Research	Research	Research
	Treatment		Research	Teaching	Teaching	Teaching
	Teaching		Treatment	Treatment	Diagnosis	Treatment
	Diagnosis	Diagnosis	Diagnosis	Diagnosis	Treatment	Diagnosis

[a] Subject is doing no teaching.
[b] Subject is doing no treatment.

The point to note about Table 1 is the negative relationship between research and diagnosis. Five place diagnosis last and one places it next to last; five list research as the most liked, and one places it next to teaching as the most liked. For these six, a dislike for diagnosis is associated with a desire to do research. For example, psychologist "B" who says that "research would be first by far," also says of diagnosis:

> If you can find a hole for diagnosis, you can put it there. After seeing 150 patients this year I don't care if I never see one again. I don't get much kick out of this service [diagnostic] function. You can have that damn testing function.

A conflict in roles is obvious when we note that five of the six are hired primarily for the diagnostic role. The exception is "F" who devotes most of his time to research. The situation confronting the other five is thus a depriving one inasmuch as the role conflict requires the performance of disliked activities while valued activities are forgone. The situation is not unlike the teaching *vs.* research dilemma of the university professor.[3] There is an important difference, however. In the university setting, the psychologist—as professor—may distribute his work and time between teaching and research with a large degree of freedom. Research is usually open to him provided he can obtain the necessary funds, often with a reduction in teaching load. Research opportunities and reduction of the testing function among Department psychologists are not so easily attained. The chief psychologist phrases the problem in the following way.

> Psychologist: The basic problem is this. In medical settings there is always a greater demand than can be met. There are always more patients than can be adequately cared for. Psychiatry is always demanding more service from psychologists than the psychologist can give. This is a realistic pressure which psychologists resist and which they have to resist. While it is recognized by psychiatrists that psychologists have to perform a service function, research is also recognized; but service receives most emphasis by psychiatry. Research and teaching are recognized; nevertheless, the underlying notion is that if the psychologist did less teaching and research there would be more time for service. What you are up against is the faculty position versus the service position. As far as the hospital administrator is concerned, he hires us to do a service function. However, we feel that we should function as faculty members, and in this should be given autonomy and independence.

> Interviewer: Faculty status would involve autonomy and independence from psychiatry?

> Psychologist: In faculty positions, as you know, the individual is autonomous. Sure, the individual faculty member has to teach a certain number of hours, he has to serve on committees, and so on, but no one tells him what to do. No one tells him what to do research on. He does research on what he wants to as

3. See Logan Wilson, *The Academic Man* (New York: Oxford University Press, 1942); and Theodore J. Caplow and Reece J. McGee, *The Academic Marketplace* (New York: Basic Books, 1958).

long as he can get the grants. The principle is upheld here but the pressure of clinical service is too great. There are just too many patients [to test]. Consequently, there is less freedom in this setting than in a purely academic setting. I think that is one reason why _____ left. There is this tendency on the part of psychologists to resist clinical service. In an academic department—psychology, history, sociology—people on the faculty, the people on the staff, determine the fate of the department. Of course, there are the deans that the heads of the departments work with, but any academic department controls its own fate. But here we are the captive fate of psychiatry. But what is involved is we are at the service of another profession with its own objective and one not identical to ours—and understandably so—and you have to fight for your life. You have to fight for research time.

In short, the *volume of work* which is the making of *another* profession restricts the psychologist's autonomy to perform the role of research. This is further indicated by the fact that, with the exception of "F," all research-oriented express a desire to have more time for research.

This conclusion does not contradict the conclusion that formal procedures surrounding the diagnostic role permit the psychologist autonomy in his performance of that role. These procedures do protect his autonomy, since the behavior of the other is controlled and regulated by organizational rules so that little difficulty occurs in the co-ordination of activities. The resident, in other words, cannot interfere with the psychologist's role performance. The performance of the diagnostic role, however, requires five psychologists to forgo performance of a more desired role—research. Consequently, a structure requiring the primary performance of the diagnostic role restricts the psychologist's autonomy to perform another role. Although formal procedures cut costs in the *specific* role of diagnosis, their more general effect is to induce costs because they prevent the performance of the research role. Simply stated, the departmental structure requires more diagnostic work of the research-oriented psychologist than he cares to do and does not permit enough time for research. Below are ways in which psychologists react to this structural dilemma in efforts to obtain more research time.

An inpatient psychologist states, "I'm actually hired as a clinician. Supposedly one day each week I spend on research and four I spend on clinical [diagnostic] work," although "I spend much more time on research than I do as a clinician." This is accomplished by "taking the research time anyway."

> Psychologist: Well, I stay away from them [staff psychiatrists]. I don't bother with the psychiatrists; I do all my socializing with the residents—I've built up some pretty good relationships with some of them. I know I'm shirking off on the ward, but a couple [of residents] cover for me. They know what I'm doing. I know I've been letting them down and they could really hang me if they wanted to. I haven't attended ward rounds for over a month. I haven't made over one trip to the ward each day for over a month. I haven't done any clinical work at all to speak of. I just try to keep from getting too far behind in the testing.

> Interviewer: By staying away from the psychiatrists and socializing with the residents, you have been able to get this extra time to do research?

> Psychologist: That's right. They cover for me. The psychiatrists don't know I haven't been around, I don't guess. They don't think much of diagnostics anyway so they don't miss me. I stay away from them.

Research grants play an important function for psychologists who want to do research. Since psychologists are paid by another profession, they are obligated to perform a diagnostic service for that profession; however, this obligation may be removed if research grants are obtained which will pay their salaries (or a portion thereof). For example, one psychologist who strongly dislikes giving diagnostic tests has been successful in getting a full-time research position.

> The money comes primarily from grants, so the research is not attached to either of the sub-departments [inpatient, outpatient, or child]. A big part of the research is being done on the outpatient service so I tend to see myself as part of the outpatient, but as far as duties are concerned with any individual department, I don't have any.

Another psychologist, who devotes one-third of his time to research, is even more explicit about this function of research grants.

> Psychologist: I got a chunk of my time allocated to the _____ project. There is an advantage in doing it this way; if you get this time allocated, it has an advantage.

Interviewer: How do you mean?

Psychologist: You have an ethical right to demand it. I can't go in and flatly tell them I demand this time for research, but since the money comes from the grant I can legally or ethically, or what have you, block off a chunk of time for research purposes. The time is mine to set aside for research; the grant is paying for it.

Research grants partially remove one of the psychologist's obligations to the Department of Psychiatry—the costly performance of diagnostic services. Accordingly, they are to be viewed as cost-reducing mechanisms.

A final method for getting more research time is to drop therapy cases. "I've refused to take on more therapy so I would have research time open." For one of the three who employs this device, it is an unsuitable solution to the dilemma. He decides, therefore, to leave the organization and accept an academic position: "This is one special reason I'm leaving—not enough time for research."

Despite the diagnostic role's restricting their freedom, five of the six research-oriented find ways to combat such restrictions; only one is unable to find a solution to the diagnosis-research dilemma. Yet, except for the two who have gotten time allocated to research grants, all are oriented away from the organization: one withdraws and the other three are making plans to do so. For these four, the cost of departmental membership outweighs the reward. For example, a psychologist, who is looking for an academic position where he will have more freedom to conduct research, remarks:

You stick around here and there's something about it—it's a stagnation kind of thing. You sit around on your ass and do a little work and draw your pay check. Advantages some see in it is you can teach on campus. But it's mostly diagnostic work—just a routine.

A major point made thus far in this book refers to the cost-reducing function of routinized, bureaucratic procedures. Up to now, however, we have been concerned with the routinization of the other's behavior. In this section attention has focused on certain "negative" effects of bureaucratic procedures when they are applied to the actor's behavior. Because he is a member of a bureaucratic organization which requires certain routine activities (diagnostic testing) from him, the psychologist is denied the freedom to which he is accustomed in a university setting. On this point, two psychologists volunteer:

> I would rather have a more *independent role.* I don't want to be dependent on their [psychiatrists'] whim. We are hired to do clinical work, and if you don't do what they want you to do, they say, come on let's quit doing so much research and teaching. If we had a more independent role, it would help, but I've gotten along with this okay [by having residents cover for him].

> The salary isn't really the thing. It's all the other things—lack of opportunity to do private practice, to consult, and no time for research. It's not just money; it's a *lack of autonomy* more than anything else.

TEACHING AND THE FUNCTION OF JOINT APPOINTMENTS

All psychologists perform a teaching role in the sense that diagnostic work in conjunction with residents is educational for residents. In addition, seven of the eight Ph.D. psychologists are engaged in more formal teaching. This consists of teaching on the campus, as well as supervising clinical psychology graduate students from the campus department who are doing internships in the Department of Psychiatry. Also, academic courses are taught to student nurses from the School of Nursing, seminars are held for psychiatric residents, and occasional lectures on diagnostic tests are given to medical students. Nevertheless, excepting the two who perform no diagnostic function, all psychologists are hired primarily for diagnostic work. None is hired primarily for teaching purposes.

In light of their academic background and tradition, however, one would expect psychologists to place a high value on the teaching role. Its value can be seen from the following table which represents the work preferences of all psychologists who have a Ph.D. (excluding the chief supervisor).

Table 2 shows that with the exception of "I," who is unable to express a hierarchy of preferences, all Ph.D.'s give high priority to teaching. Excepting "F," who devotes most of his time to research, however, all are hired primarily for diagnostic services. Consequently, one would expect psychologists who prefer one form of work but do another to incur costs. Yet there is a cost-reducing structure: all Ph.D.'s have faculty appointments in the

TABLE 2   RANK ORDER WORK PREFERENCE OF ALL PSYCHOLOGISTS
WHO HAVE THE PH.D. DEGREE[a]

Psychologist	"C"	"D"	"E"	"F"	"G"	"H"	"I"[b]
Rank	Teaching	Research	Research	Research	Teaching	Teaching	
	Research	Teaching	Teaching	Teaching	Research	Diagnosis	
Order	Treatment	Treatment	Diagnosis	Treatment	Diagnosis	Treatment	
	Diagnosis	Diagnosis	Treatment	Diagnosis	Treatment	Research	

[a] Excluding the supervisor.
[b] Performing no teaching function and unable to rank order functions.

campus Department of Psychology. All except "I" teach courses in the campus department, and all supervise clinical psychology interns. Without these opportunities it is questionable if many psychologists would remain in the Department. Psychologist "D" states, for example, "most of us would quit" if psychologists were deprived of teaching psychology students, since "the teaching function is one of the most important to us." Joint appointment in the Department of Psychiatry and Department of Psychology is, then, a structural mechanism reducing costs for the psychologists.

Nevertheless, teaching opportunities are still too limited for "C," who has decided to leave the Department. Such limitations must be viewed in terms of the Department's structural restraint on his autonomy to teach as well as to do more research.

> Important is the time it takes to devote to my seminar [on campus]. It takes a heck of a lot of preparation, and I felt that I had a lack of time to devote to it. I couldn't cut down on this time. Another factor is the fact that no consideration is given by psychiatrists, well, [Department Head], to our teaching. Time isn't allowed, and also no recognition that there was a great deal of extra time being spent on it. The relevance of all this to my leaving is, by switching over I have more latitude in my time commitment. I will be able to teach—I'm to be teaching two courses—and there will be more freedom to do research.

SUMMARY AND CONCLUSION

Pursuing further the relationship between social norms and cost reduction, we find in the analysis of the psychologist's diagnostic role additional support for the general hypothesis that social norms function to reduce costs and substitute for informal influence. The hypothesis must be further specified, however. It is only when norms controlling the other's behavior aid the actor in obtaining certain values that they reduce his costs. Therefore, alter's deviation may actually be cost-reducing if the rule hinders ego's attainment of values, in the present case, autonomy.

Comments from a psychiatric resident suggest that rules which have a cost-reducing effect for one actor may also have a cost-inducing effect for another. Organizational rules surrounding referrals for psychological testing permitted the psychologist autonomy in his role performance, but deprived the resident of it in his role performance. In addition, analysis of the psychologist's research-diagnosis dilemma discloses that the performance of one role (diagnosis)—where costs have been very much eliminated—may have a cost-inducing effect because it deprives one of performing a more desired role (research). And finally, because of the high value teaching has for psychologists, joint appointments in the departments of psychiatry and psychology function to reduce costs for psychologists.

In general, the major source of the psychologists' difficulties— insofar as the performance of their instrumental roles are concerned—appears to lie in the psychiatrists' demand for more diagnostic testing. The difficulty does not lie in conflicting opinions about the nature of specific roles, as was the case with the social workers, but in how much emphasis to give to different roles. The psychiatrists understandably wanted more diagnostic services; equally understandable is the psychologists' desire to conduct more research.

7 PSYCHIATRIC NURSING: ROLE CONFLICT AND MAINTAINING POWER STRATEGIES

Two major points have been made in the previous three chapters. One, under noninstitutionalized conditions, ego has the problem of influencing alter's use of facilities, and two types of power strategies were identified: implementing cost-inducing and structural cost-reducing. Second, when relationships are institutionalized, the normative control of alter's use of facilities reduces ego's costs. In this chapter, the power strategy concept will be used to describe actions taking place in a firmly institutionalized relationship.

Data for this chapter are based on a study of sixteen nurses, who differ from the other three professions in important ways. First, nurses have a longer tradition of working with medical doctors than the other professions. Also, unlike the recreator and social workers but similar to the psychologists, there are formal definitions of the nurses' role along with formal definitions of the residents' duties vis-à-vis the nurses. In accordance with the institution's objective of creating a therapeutic *milieu* for its patients, nurses are required to relate to patients according to the patients' therapeutic needs, and residents are to instruct nurses in how they should do this. In addition to issuing written orders to nurses, residents provide verbal instructions during ward rounds, team meetings, and throughout the day as the resident and nurse are in continuous contact on the ward. Consequently, nurses experience neither the social workers' nor recreator's difficulties of doctors' not using their services, nor the recreator's problem of residents' not knowing of her existence. Relative to the recreator and social workers, nurses experience a more highly institutionalized relationship with residents.[1]

This chapter, therefore, will not focus on problems stemming from insufficient institutionalization. Instead, it will deal with nurses' reactions—particularly power strategies—to a role conflict. To understand the nature of this conflict and the influence attempts to which it gives rise, it is necessary to describe four important features of the nurses' instrumental role.

COMPONENTS OF THE NURSE'S INSTRUMENTAL ROLE

The following description of the nurse's role should not be considered a complete analysis of the role of psychiatric nurse, since only those aspects are described which are particularly relevant to her relationship with the psychiatric resident and to *one* form of role conflict.

Objective of Helping the Patient

Nurses, like doctors, are morally obligated to help patients recover from their illness. The present group of nurses indicate their acceptance ("internalization") of this obligation in two different ways. First, fourteen of fifteen state that their objective is to help patients "get well," to "return to normal," to "return to society," or to "get back on their feet and be socially accepted again."[2]

1. Although Brown's description of the resident-nurse relationship during the early days of the inpatient service indicates that this may not have always been the case, see Robert G. Brown, "Problems of Social Organization in a New Psychiatric Inpatient Service" (unpublished Ph.D. dissertation, Department of Sociology and Anthropology, University of North Carolina, 1960).
2. These responses are replies to the question: "What specifically are you— as a psychiatric nurse—trying to accomplish in the performance of your nursing duties?" The fifteenth—who states that the nurse's objective is "to carry out the doctor's care and treatment plan"—implies a similar objective since the doctor is ethically obligated to facilitate the patient's recovery. Although sixteen nurses were interviewed, only fifteen were asked the above question.

Their moral commitment to the patient is further indicated by their disapproval of a form of treatment administered to patients for research purposes. Residents are required to place all patients needing day-time sedation on a drug research project where patients receive one of three sedation drugs or an inert placebo. The objective of the research is to ascertain the precise effects certain drugs have on patients' behavior. It is designed so that no one, including the patient's doctor, knows what drug the patient receives. Such procedure is necessary to control for possible contaminating effects due to patients' responding in terms of their knowledge of the drug's alleged effects, and effects due to ward personnel's interacting with patients in terms of their expectations of the drug's effects. Therefore, when doctors place patients on the project, they must "prescribe in the blind": which drug the patient receives (or whether he receives an inert placebo) is determined by random placement and not by the doctor's evaluation of the patient's therapeutic needs.

In reply to the query of how they felt about the project, thirteen of sixteen nurses express disapproval. Their moral obligation to the patient's welfare is indicated by nine nurses who disapprove of the project because the patient may be given a placebo which will not help him; because the drugs are administered by random placement and not according to the patient's needs; and because the project drugs are slow acting, thus leading to unnecessary expense to the patient. The nurse's moral obligation to the patient rather than to scientific research is aptly stated in the following reply:

> It's the drug that happens to come up that the patient gets. I disagree very strongly with this. If it's not helping the patient, *we have no right* to keep him on it. It's okay for people wanting to know about drugs, they want to know about them and that's all right, but what about the patient? *It's the patient's welfare that is utmost,* not knowing about some drug.

Interpersonal Relationship with Patients

Several recent studies of psychiatric nurses find a major aspect of the nurse's role to involve interpersonal relationships with patients, through which the patients' emotional needs are to be met.[3] That the present group of nurses also includes an inter-personal nurse-patient relationship in their role can be seen from the following data.

In discussing the activities they perform, the sixteen nurses mention forty-five different activities which range from ordering supplies to interpreting the patient's behavior to the patient. Table 3 below lists all activities mentioned by more than two nurses. Clearly, some activities do not necessarily involve an

TABLE 3 ACTIVITIES MENTIONED BY THREE OR MORE NURSES
AS DUTIES OF THE PSYCHIATRIC NURSE

Activity Mentioned	Number Who Mention the Activity[a]	Number Who Consider Activity to be the "Major," "Primary," or "Most Important" Activity[b]
Talking and Listening to Patients	9	4
Observation of Patients' Behavior	7	3
Getting Patients into Activities	7	1
Giving Medication	6[c]	0
Reporting Observation of Patients to Doctors	5	0
Establishing or Maintaining a "Relationship" with Patients	4	4
Recording Observations of Patients in Patients' Charts	4[d]	0
Accepting the Patient	3	0
Carrying out Doctor's Treatment Plan in Nurse-Patient Relationship	3	1
Supporting Patients	3	0

[a] In response to the question: "Would you discuss with me the kinds of activities you perform as a psychiatric nurse?"

[b] Information volunteered in response to question (a), or in answer to the question: "What do you consider to be the most important nursing activity?"

[c] Three mention activity as "peripheral" or as "not important"; one mentions activity as "routine."

[d] Two mention activity as "routine."

3. Harry W. Martin and Ida Harper Simpson, *Patterns of Psychiatric Nursing: A Survey of Psychiatric Nursing in North Carolina* (Chapel Hill: Institute for Research in Social Science, 1956); Brown, "Problems of Social Organization . . ."; and Dorothea Scott, "The Relation of the Uniform to the Professional Self-Image of the Psychiatric Nurse" (unpublished Master's thesis, Department of Sociology and Anthropology, University of North Carolina, 1960).

interpersonal relationship with patients—the activities of giving medication and recording observations, for example. In both of these cases, however, nurses refer to the activity as "not important" or as "routine." Also, observing patient's behavior and reporting these observations do not mean that one *must* have an interpersonal relationship with the patient. However, it is the type of activity mentioned as the "major," "primary," or "most important" nursing activity that is the major feature to note. In ten out of thirteen instances, the activity definitely involves a relationship with patients; the only activity not necessarily entailing an interpersonal relationship is "observation of patients' behavior"—mentioned by three nurses. In addition, one further interpersonal activity—"comforting patients," mentioned by only one nurse is listed as the most important of the nursing duties.

There are two additional sources of data which also point to the nurse's involvement in interpersonal relationships with patients. First, twelve of thirteen nurses replied in the affirmative when asked if they found the psychologists' duties of use in the performance of their nursing duties.[4] In general, nurses state that psychological test reports (both written and verbal) afford them a better understanding of the patient and the way he thinks, feels, and acts. To be concerned with such matters, at best, only implies interpersonal involvement with the patient. More relevant are the responses in reply to probes or as voluntary elaborations of the above general response. These responses are as follows: four report that tests help them know what to look for and to be aware of in the patient's behavior; five state the reports enable them to know what to expect from the patient; one claims that they "help me to relate to the patient—they help me to understand what it is that is bothering the patient"; one replies that tests "help me to know more how to act toward the patient"; and, finally, one finds them useful in revealing suicidal thoughts. With the exception of the latter, all are explicit expressions of the kinds of concern all persons have in interpersonal relationships: knowing what to expect from or what to be aware of in regard

4. Thirteen nurses were asked: "Do you find the duties of the psychologist of any help in the performance of your nursing duties?" Three nurses had been interviewed before the question's value for obtaining an indication of the nurse's role conception was recognized.

to the other's behavior. For example, one nurse reports that psychological tests are helpful because:

> You just know what to expect. Just knowing this [test report] you know what to expect from the patient. You know what kinds of behavior to expect from the patient, what kinds of things to look for from them.

Another says:

> If a patient is a psychopath, we can expect just about anything from him. The psychologist's report helps us to know more what to expect from the patient. A patient may be a suicidal and we might not know, but if the psychological tests bring this out we know what to expect from him.

Additional data indicating the nurses' interpersonal involvement with patients are reasons given for disapproving the previously described drug project. Not only is the project opposed on moral grounds, but eight nurses indicate that the administration of an unknown drug interferes with the nurse-patient relationship. When unknown drugs are given, nurses do not know what to expect from patients: "I don't like to give any kind of drug that I don't know what the effects will be"; "my objection is only in relation to not knowing what to expect from the patient." Some nurses have a moral objection as well. "My main complaints are that it's doubtful if it's going to help the patient, and you just never know what to expect."

The above three sources of data are, then, consistent with previous research which indicates the role of psychiatric nurse involves interpersonal relationships with patients. For example, in previous research on nurses in the present setting, Robert G. Brown concludes that although nurses may lack a precise definition of their role, they do see it in terms of "relating to patients."[5] Scott's study also finds these nurses conceiving themselves as performing a "function of an interpersonal nature": understanding the emotional needs of patients and meeting these needs through relationships with them.[6]

5. Brown, "Problems of Social Organization. . . ."
6. Scott, "The Relation of the Uniform . . . of the Psychiatric Nurse."

Power of the Resident

Although the nurse's role involves an interpersonal relationship with the patient, her background and training may not have prepared her for this role. Her task is to meet the emotional needs of patients, but she has received little training in the skills necessary to recognize, identify, and meet these needs. Accordingly, in his study of the early days of the inpatient service, Brown notes that the nurse faces a dilemma: "She may know that the expectations of her role include recognizing the emotional needs of patients and meeting those needs by 'relating to patients'; but she is not likely to have the requisite knowledge and understanding of these skills to play this role accurately or with any degree of comfort." Consequently, the nurse turns to the resident for direction and guidance to determine how she shall "relate to patients." [7] One nurse says, for example:

> He [resident] gives us his orders and what he wants us to do with the patient. We have discussions with him and through this find out how we can help the patients cope with their emotional problems. Sometimes we have to use our own judgment in this, but mostly the doctor lays out the outline for us.

The need for direction from the resident is especially apparent when it is recognized that the nurse is with the patient eight hours a day: "We are with them [patients] eight hours a day and *we need this direction*"; "we are with the patient eight hours a day, but the doctor—*he's our guide.*"

Because of her dependence on the doctor, the nurse needs a close working relationship with him, closer perhaps than is true of nurse-doctor relationship in other areas of medicine. A nurse formulates the differences in the following manner.

> Here in psychiatry the relationships between the nurse and doctor have to be closer. The nurse and resident really have to work together more than in other services because the nurse is with the patient eight hours and knows more about him. It is not like treating a physical illness, or an operation of some sort. Since we are with the patient so much, the doctor must tell us how we should handle the patient while we are with him.

7. Brown, "Problems of Social Organization . . . ," p. 83.

Other examples of the nurses' expressed dependency on the resident are as follows:

> [The resident] has to tell us ways of dealing with the patient. Whether you might be firm with the patient or be lenient. Whether to push him into activities; what you might do with him.

> They give us a nursing care plan which is most helpful in enabling us to know how to deal with problems that may arise from a patient. It helps you to know what to do. To give an example, a patient could become very dependent, so you must know whether it's desirable or not to have this kind of relationship. It might be that it would be good for him to have this kind of relationship, but you don't know unless the doctor gives you his order.

> Since we are with the patient so much, the doctor must tell us how we should handle the patient while we are with him. Of course, a lot of times we will have an ordinary relationship with them like with any ordinary person. But a lot of times there will be patients that we won't know exactly how to handle. Like we may bring up topics to talk about that we shouldn't. And the doctor will often know this; he will know from his sessions with the patient, and he can tell us to stay away from subjects like this—about his family, his children, or maybe something else. Or maybe we should talk about these things with the patient. If we know this, we can gear the conversation so as to not antagonize the patient or bother him.

Clearly what the nurse does in her relationship with the patient is very much dependent on what the resident instructs her to do. Within the conceptual framework of this study, the resident is an important source of facilities for the nurse; it is on the basis of information and direction provided by him that she relates to patients and thereby attempts to meet their emotional needs. Not knowing how to perform this role adequately, the nurse *needs* to get orders, directives, and information pertaining to patients; without this guidance she does not know whether her relationship with patients is facilitating or hindering their recovery. Consequently, the resident has a high degree of power over her.

It is important to note that residents supply direction and guidance in verbal as well as written form. They issue verbal instructions during team meetings and ward rounds, and in response to questions nurses have throughout the day.

> [In addition to written orders] we have team meetings. Here we discuss the individual patient the doctor is in charge of. They explain why a patient behaves the way he does on the ward. He acts sort of like a guide for us. Usually they are there if we have trouble or have a question to ask—we can go to them and ask them how we should handle a particular situation. If a patient asks us something and we don't know how we should answer, we can go to him and find out how we should answer the patient.

Several nurses volunteer that verbal instructions given through face-to-face contacts are actually more useful than written orders. A head nurse says, for example, "There's not much in the form of written orders" since most directions come through face-to-face contact by "sitting down and talking to him, and in team meetings." Another states that written instructions are useful but "not as much as team meetings, and when we sit down and talk about the patient—like if I have a question or if he wants to tell me something about the patient." Another head nurse states:

> They will sometimes give a written order on how we might best treat the patient. But usually we just ask him, or he will tell us in team meetings. Most things are not written out in detail. When they are written out, they are usually too general to be of much help. When we ask the doctor something we just sit down and talk about it.

The importance of face-to-face contact with the resident in determining the character of the nurses' interpersonal relationship with the patient is further indicated by such comments as the following:

> They [residents] are especially helpful in team meetings in telling what's going on with the patient. This helps us to understand the patient and know better what to expect. In team meetings or when he's on the ward, we can ask him what we should do if we are having trouble relating to the patient. He can act as an advisor like this.

> We have team meetings and we can find out a lot about the patient, both from what he tells us voluntarily and in answer

to our questions. They let us know what we can expect from the patient. Whether we should push them in activities or not, and whether they will rebel if we do.

Team meetings are the most important thing. Here they explain what they are doing with their patients, and what they want us to do with the patients. They tell us the nursing care plan in team meetings. We have to have these every week; otherwise orders aren't explicit enough, and we don't know what we should be doing.

We have team meetings and rounds and he will point these things out [explain patient's behavior] for us then. When he's around the ward, we can just ask him what he wants, or we will ask him to explain something about the patient.

These data reveal more specifically the nature of the nurse's dependence on the resident. Her interpersonal relationship with the patient depends upon face-to-face relationships with residents, relationships in which patients' illnesses and appropriate methods of treatment are discussed. No claim is made that face-to-face discussions are more important than written orders and directions, although several nurses volunteer that they are. The point to note is the fact that nurses and residents are in continuous face-to-face relationship and that nurses value this type relationship.

Authority of the Resident

Not only is the nurse dependent on the resident's orders; she is also responsible for carrying them out. She is subordinate to the doctor relative to the responsibility for the patient and the doctor's authority; she must obey his "orders." In a sense, the nurse's function may actually be described as the responsibility to carry out the doctor's orders. A head nurse puts this the following way:

As I see it, the function of the psychiatric nurse, the major function, is to carry out the doctor's care and treatment plan. The doctor is head of the team and it is the nurse's responsibility to carry out his treatment plan. She is on the ward twenty-four hours a day and is someone that the patient can talk with. She can talk to him about his problems. She is the go between the doctor and the patient. She relates to the patient so as to support him when he needs it, and so on. She relates to him in terms of the doctor's care plan.

It is essential to keep in mind the difference between the authority and power of the resident. Regarding his power, the nurse is dependent on the resident's directions and orders—she *needs* directions to determine how she shall perform her interpersonal role with the patient. Regarding authority, the nurse is *responsible* for conforming to the doctor's directives and "orders." Otherwise stated, authority is a normative phenomenon; power is not. The general norms of medicine ethically obligate the nurse to carry out the resident's orders: Norms define the doctor as the superior and he makes the treatment decisions because of his greater knowledge and competence. On the other hand, the nature of the work gives the doctor (resident) power over the nurse: With his superior knowledge, the resident is a source to whom the nurse must turn to determine how she shall relate to patients. In any *concrete* course of action (a particular nurse-patient relationship), the nurse does, of course, respond to both orders. The distinction is analytic: It refers to different aspects or properties of the nurse's action in her relationship with the patient. Nevertheless, the distinction is crucial. Its importance will be outlined shortly.

ROLE CONFLICT: CONFLICT BETWEEN NORMATIVE ORDERS

This description of the nurse's role reveals that there are two moral or ethical principles involved in the nurse's role performance: the obligation to help the patient and the obligation and responsibility to carry out the resident's orders. Certainly, few persons in the field of medicine would question the nurse's obligation to conform to these two principles. The question arises, however: What do nurses do when these two principles conflict? For example, what does she do when she thinks the doctor's orders are unsuitable for meeting the patient's therapeutic needs? Such conflicts are especially likely when the nurse-patient relationship is emphasized as an aspect of the treatment process because the nurse is with the patient over an eight-hour period, while the doctor is with him only during the therapeutic hour; also, most doctors on the inpatient service are first-year residents and, therefore, possess little psychiatric experience.[8] Consequently, the nurse may sometimes think she knows more than the doctor about proper treatment procedures for particular patients. Brown formulates the nurses' conflict this way: At times nurses "felt the decisions made by residents were not the proper ones, yet they were constrained by medical norms from refusing to obey such orders. Thus, nurses sometimes found themselves to be in role-conflict situations." [9]

The affirmative reply of fifteen out of sixteen nurses when asked, "Have residents ever given you an order which you think is contrary to the patient's welfare?", indicates the existence of this conflict. Nurses report two types of reaction to this conflict: conforming to the resident's authority and attempts to influence his orders.

CONFORMING TO THE RESIDENT'S AUTHORITY

Four report that they usually carry out the order as stated by the doctor. When questioned why they did this when they thought the order was not the proper one, they replied as follows:

I don't know really. This was the way I was taught—to carry out the doctor's orders. I guess this is the reason; I've never thought about it.

I don't really know. It just is, well, that's the way it is. It's sort of an unwritten law to do it this way. The nurse accepts it that way. She takes her orders from the doctor and carries them out. It may be that I do not agree with him, but it's his decision and so I go on and carry it out the way he thinks it should be. I guess you can say I act as if I agree with him.

It's his decision. It's the nurse's responsibility to carry out his orders. If that's what he thinks should be done, I am supposed to carry it out. We had a case not long ago when I disagreed. This one patient the doctor had on out-alone privileges and I didn't think she should be, but I felt that this should be his decision so I didn't say anything. For the most part I think the doctor-nurse relationship is very good. I don't have any conflict with

8. For a discussion of this problem see Harvey L. Smith, "Professional Strains and the Hospital Context," in Milton Greenblatt, Daniel J. Levinson, and Richard H. Williams (eds.), *The Patient and the Mental Hospital* (Glencoe: The Free Press, 1957), p. 7.
9. Brown, "Problems of Social Organization . . . ," p. 51.

them. If they give an order that I disagree with, I go along with it because that's supposed to be his decision. The nurse is supposed to carry his decision out.

Finally, one nurse states that she obeys the order because of her training. "In nursing school they tell you how much authority the doctor has and that what he says goes."

These nurses, then, give priority to their obedience to the doctor's orders over what they consider best for the patient. Their responses are explicit manifestations of the internalization of the nurse-doctor authority relationship which implies that the doctor is more knowledgeable and competent than the nurse.

POWER STRATEGIES

More interesting, for purposes of this study, are the eleven nurses who do not give the doctor's order priority over what they feel are the patient's interests. Instead of complying when they disagree, they attempt to influence a change in the treatment order. The problem is, then, one of subordinates influencing their superior. A nurse formulates the problem in the following way:

The doctor is above me and here I am down here trying to get him to do what I want him to do. I can't *tell* him.

Three different types of influence attempts are reported.

Tertius Gaudens

Nine nurses report going to the head nurse, chief resident, or ward chief and letting him take the matter up with the resident. For example:

I will go to the ward chief and tell him what the situation is. Then the ward chief can take it up with him. Then in ward rounds or in his sessions with him he will make suggestions.

Another states:

Perhaps he would place a patient on precaution, and maybe we think it would be more upsetting to the patient to place him on precaution. Or maybe he would want a patient to have sedation at night, rather than letting the patient try to sleep without sedation. If we disagree, we will go to the chief resident. Then we let the chief resident iron it out with the doctor.

Being subordinate, the nurse cannot openly contradict the resident, but she does have access to channels of authority above him which she may use to influence his decision. Although subject to his authority, she goes to the resident's superior and gets "around it": "You go to the ward chief and work around it that way."

Reporting Observations that are
Contrary to the Doctor's Order

Because nurses are with patients eight hours a day, they observe many aspects of their behavior. Consequently, eight nurses, when they disagree with the doctor's treatment decision, attempt to effect a change in treatment procedures by confronting the resident with aspects of the patient's behavior that suggest some other treatment plan is indicated. For example:

> I approach him by telling him about the patient's behavior. The nurse sees more of the patient's behavior than the doctor sees. We see them eight hours a day and he only sees them one hour. I just tell him what I have observed if I think the order is wrong. I just point out the patient's behavior that I have observed.

By so confronting the resident, the nurse expresses her disapproval of his treatment plan. One states, "I let him know what my feelings are," not by openly disagreeing with his order, but by confronting him with aspects of the patient's behavior which indicate the order is inappropriate—"I will disagree by letting him know what I observe." Another nurse says:

> I go to him and tell him this: I see where you have given patient so-and-so such-and-such in the order. I won't disagree with him, but I will know something about the patient, so I will tell him things about the patient that are contrary to the order given. Just let him know about these other things in hopes that he will change the order. I will merely tell him things about the patient that are contrary to the order.

As a case in point, the above nurse mentions that residents often prescribe drugs unnecessarily. In such cases, she reacts "by approaching the doctor and asking him how he feels about the patient not getting any better. I point out that the patient is banging himself around and that the drug is not doing any good."

The strategy of *tertius gaudens* is possible because of the hierarchical nature of the medical social structure, i.e., nurse-resident-chief resident. In that case the nurse goes to a superior *human* agent to exert influence. In the present case, she appeals to what Simmel has called an "impersonal objective principle" which is superior to both subordinate and superordinate.[10] By confronting the resident with aspects of the patient's behavior which indicate the present treatment plan is inadequate, the nurse appeals to the impersonal principle of patient welfare— to which both she and the resident are subordinate. It is, therefore, a symbolic form of *tertius gaudens*.[11] The concept of superiority and subordination in the resident-nurse relationship "is modified by the fact that in its entirety it is subsidiary to an ideal purpose" [12]—patient welfare.

Further remarks by Simmel concerning the moral aspects of "impersonal objective principles" provide additional insight into this phenomenon. Of these principles, he states:

In the moral consciousness we feel ourselves subject to a decree which does not appear to be issued by any personal human power; we hear the voice of conscience only in ourselves. . . . [It is] gradually bred into individuals as an instinct, so that it asserts itself as a peculiar autonomous impression . . . [such that] the social . . . is completely grown into the individual himself. [The principle is thus] changed into a subjective imperative, which thus presents subordination of the individual to the conditions of the life of his group, in the form of obedience to an ideal impersonal principle.[13]

The "impersonal objective principle" of patient welfare subordinates and elicits a moral commitment from residents, as it does from most physicians. And although the nurse, as a "personal human power," does not issue this principle to the resident, she can re-awaken his "voice of conscience" by (implicitly) confronting him with it; and, in so doing, she controls—or attempts

10. Georg Simmel, "Superiority and Subordination in Social Relationships," in Edgar F. Borgatta and Henry J. Meyer, *Sociological Theory: Present-Day Sociology from the Past* (New York: Alfred A. Knopf, 1956), p. 189.
11. Harvey L. Smith is to be credited with this interpretation.
12. Simmel, "Superiority and Subordination . . . ," p. 191.
13. *Ibid.*, p. 189.

to control—his behavior. Thus, what is one man's value (conscience) may become another man's power.[14]

Asking Questions

Finally, four nurses state that they ask residents questions about the order indicating they do not understand it. Rather than telling them what she thinks about the order or what she thinks it should be, one nurse says:

> For example, a lot of residents like to give the patients sedation. If I don't think the patient should have sedation, I will ask if this was intended in the order or should it be something else. Or I might say that I thought it would be thus and so. If he puts something in the order that I disagree with, I will sometimes say, I've never seen it like this before. Work around it this way. But, here again, I'm asking. Yeah, it's a matter of questioning, rather than coming right out and telling him. You have to do it this way—you have to be more tactful. I can't come right out and tell the doctor what I think the order should be.

Others indicate that they sometimes combine this approach with the relating of information about the patient's behavior that is contrary to the doctor's order.

> I will just ask him a question and then have him answer. Or we can relate a specific incidence of the patient's behavior—we are with him eight hours a day and so we know more about the patient's behavior than the resident, and then tell how we handled it, and then ask if this was right and, if not, how we should have handled it. I will ask him about the order. I will just say that there is something I don't understand and then point out something about the patient's behavior.

Another states:

> I will just ask him about the case. Like, I have a question I want to discuss with you about patient so-and-so. And then I tell him what my observations are. He might accept this and change the order.

Here we have a very interesting technique of control. The nurse knows the doctor is wrong, or at least she thinks he is.

14. Although, in this case, the nurse's values are the same as the doctor's—both are subordinate to the value ("objective impersonal principle") of patient welfare.

Accordingly, she could, in terms of the legitimate order (patient welfare), explicitly disagree with him. Instead, she plays a naïve role: She indicates she does not understand the order, asks if it were intended, or indicates that she has never seen it that way. It is then hoped that the doctor's "explanation" will consist of a change in the order.

The subordinate's asking questions in order to control his superior is a relatively unexplored phenomenon. Although it is a simple phenomenon, it may still be an important medium of influence. It deserves greater attention in sociological and social-psychological research—more than we have given to it here.

At this point a pertinent question is: Are these three types of actions conforming behavior or deviant behavior? Since they represent a "pattern of behavior" not unlike the "J-curve" [15] of conforming behavior—eleven of fifteen nurses engage in them—one might be disposed to infer that a social norm or rule prescribes them. Thus, they would be actions that correspond to social rules which define the nurse's role. Certainly, they cannot be considered deviant behavior for they are carried out in the interest of the patient—a major normative principle of the nurse's role. At the same time, however, they question the legitimacy of the resident's order; accordingly, they might be considered deviant actions.

Correctly viewed, they are neither conforming nor deviant behavior. They are actions caused by conflict between two normative principles of the nurse's role: the patient's welfare and the doctor's authority. Both principles are components of the definition of the nurse role, but the influence attempts are not specified in that definition. The definition does not say that the nurse should try to influence the doctor's decision, nor how she should go about this when she does try. Therefore, they are not prescribed role behavior. [16]

Greater understanding of these acts can be obtained if they

15. Floyd H. Allport, "The J-Curve Hypothesis of Conforming Behavior," *Journal of Social Psychology*, V (1934), 141-83.
16. That residents may not accept the nurse's influence attempts as legitimate is illustrated by an occurrence reported in Brown, "Problems of Social Organization. . . ." A resident, upon discovering that a nurse had gone to the ward chief to report what she felt was an "incorrect" treatment decision, expressed his resentment and displeasure at nurse's "going over the doctor's head."

are classified as power strategies: acts designed to influence another, but acts that are oriented to, rather than in conformity with, institutionalized normative orders. Since the nurses' strategies attempt to influence a change in the doctor's order, they are not in conformity with his authority. This is not to say that they are expressions of disrespect for his authority, however, for they are oriented to his authority. Although nurses may think they know more than residents about specific patients, they do not act as if they do. For example: "In most cases he will know more about the patient, but after all we are with the patient eight hours a day and we'll know more in certain cases. *But this doesn't mean that we can tell the doctor what he should do.*" Influence attempts are exerted instead. These influence attempts are also expressions of respect for the doctor's superiority. An example will illuminate. A nurse thinks that the resident often prescribes drugs when they are not indicated. She tries to get him to revoke his decision by asking him questions about the patient and then relating something about the patient's behavior which suggests the drug is not helping. She will not tell the resident that she actually thinks drug treatment is not the proper treatment because of her respect for him.

Nurse: I would say that I *wonder* if the drug is helping the patient. I may think that the drug isn't helping the patient, but I wouldn't tell him that.

Interviewer: Why not? You say you usually know more about the patient's behavior than the doctor. Why don't you tell him you think it's a bad order?

Nurse: Because I respect him. If I don't respect him as a person, I respect his title.

Interviewer: What's the title got to do with preventing you from saying what you think?

Nurse: (Smiles.) Because he's a doctor and I'm a nurse.

Interviewer: What does that mean?

Nurse: That means that he's more educated and knows more and is more able to handle the situation than I, or at least he's supposed to be.

Another nurse, in commenting on why she does not openly express her opinion to the doctor, states quite similarly:

> Nurse: I don't think this is right. I don't think a nurse should tell a doctor if she disagrees with him.
>
> Interviewer: Why not?
>
> Nurse: I guess it's just my feeling that the doctor should know more about the patient than I.

We thus have the situation where the resident is *defined* as possessing superior knowledge to the nurse, but where the nurse believes that she knows more about the needs of specific patients. The doctor-nurse relationship is thus threatened with what might be termed a role reversal: the subordinate believes himself superior to the superordinate. A staff psychiatrist puts it this way:

> The resident-nurse relationship is a sticky one. The resident is supposed to know more than the nurse, but this very generally isn't the case, not in the beginning of the resident's training, anyway. The resident feels this; the nurse knows it.

Nevertheless, the nurse must not indicate that she thinks she knows more than the resident. The above psychiatrist continues: "If the resident makes a mistake or does something wrong, the nurse knows. She can't correct him because he's a doctor and is supposed to know more than she." The role structure must be preserved. The nurse must *orient* her influence attempts to this role structure.

> I might, and do, try to get him to change his plan, but I won't make it look like I think he should change it.

The nurses' power strategies must be viewed as forms of deference behavior. Deference refers to an individual's expressing sentiments of "regard," "respect," and "appreciation" for another and his role responsibilities.[17] Clearly, the nurses' power strategies are acts of deference. For example, a nurse, in commenting on her attempt to influence the resident's decision, states:

> I have to be careful. I can't let it look like I am trying to tell him what to do. I have to approach him in a manner so that it looks like I am not telling him.

17. Erving Goffman, "The Nature of Deference and Demeanor," *American Anthropologist,* LVIII (1956), 473-502.

Although the influence attempts originate with the nurse's thinking she is better informed than the resident, they are also expressions of respect and regard for the doctor's superiority, for in being "careful" the nurse orients her actions to the doctor's superior status. We may also view these acts as "avoidance rituals" [18]—taking care not to infringe upon the duties and responsibilities of another role performer. Accordingly, these nurses, like the previous four, indicate that they too have internalized the authority structure of the resident-nurse role relationship.

In light of this analysis, these acts serve to reinforce the status relationship between nurse and resident. For the nurse to be "careful" not to let the resident think she is trying to tell him what to do is precisely one way in which the doctor's superiority is socially confirmed. However, these acts of deference are more; they are also attempts to influence.

> Nurse: There are times when I disapprove [of his order] and will try to do something about it.
>
> Interviewer: How do you do this?
>
> Nurse: I will try to suggest things to him without it sounding like an order. If a doctor forgets something, I will ask him if he would mind doing it. Like forgetting an order. Or, if he is not treating the patient right, I will ask him what he thinks about doing something else.
>
> Interviewer: It seems that you are doing this in somewhat of an asking capacity.
>
> Nurse: Yes, I think that puts it about right. You see, I'm still a nurse. I may know more than the resident, but he's still the doctor and I can't tell him what to do. I have to try to *get* him to do what I want him to do. I can't order him.

The nurse's power strategies are influence at the price of deference. She attempts to exchange deference behavior for a change in doctors' treatment decisions.

MAINTAINING COST-PREVENTING STRATEGIES

A distinction has been made between implementing cost-inducing and structural cost-reducing power strategies. The nurses'

18. *Ibid.*

strategies are clearly not of the structural type: none is concerned with changing or modifying the structure of the nurse-resident relationship (e.g., none is an attempt to evoke a norm). As we said, they reinforce this relationship instead. Their distinction from implementing strategies is less clear. In fact, *tertius gaudens* was classified as an implementing strategy in the analyses of recreation and social service. Nevertheless, the nurses' strategies are sufficiently different from implementing strategies to warrant separate classification.

These strategies, being forms of deference, are behaviors which pay respect to convention—the belief that the doctor is superior to the nurse. Erving Goffman states that deference also functions to confirm the conceptions of selves.[19] Thus, the nurses' influence attempts may be interpreted as expressions of respect for the superiority and greater competence of the resident: she confirms the resident's self-image that he is superior to the nurse. Goffman's formulation helps us to understand some of the elements involved in the nurse's strategies, but they do not reveal their precise function for the *nurse*.

Rose Laub Coser observes that deference performs still another function. It does "not merely serve to pay respect to other individuals or to pay tribute to convention, but (serves) to maintain the relational system."[20] According to this hypothesis, the nurse's power strategies function to maintain the doctor-nurse relationship. As was indicated above, in this relationship the resident possesses a high degree of power over the nurse: the nurse must turn to him for directives and guidance to determine how she shall "relate to" patients. These directives cannot be issued solely through impersonal formal written specifications, but must be supplemented by face-to-face discussions between nurse and resident. The relational system is, then, a continuous face-to-face one. Its continuity is difficult if the nurse-resident relationship is strained.

> Nurse: I think that there should be a good relationship between the nurse and the doctor. Because if there are hard feelings, neither will want to help the other with the patient.

19. *Ibid.*
20. Rose Laub Coser, "Insulation from Observability and Types of Social Conformity," *American Sociological Review,* XXVI (1961), 31.

Interviewer: What would a good relationship with the resident be like?

Nurse: Well, you should be able to talk to him. I think he should discuss with the nurse why he does something. It helps you to understand him better, and to understand the patient better.

One method of creating strain (e.g., "hard feelings") in this relationship is for the nurse to try to invert the status differences —e.g., to question the resident's superior knowledge and competence by questioning his order. Understandably, the resident may become angry with the nurse; he may proceed to put her in her "place." In a previous study of the resident-nurse relationship in this setting, it was found that residents withdrew from their relationship with the nurse when the latter questioned their orders.[21] This, however, deprives the nurse of something she *values*—a close relationship with the doctor. When she questions the resident's order, she runs the risk of incurring costs—forgoing the value of a close doctor-nurse relationship. Consequently, she would not understand the patient's behavior, she would not know what to talk to him about, she would not know what to expect from him—in general, she would not know how she should relate to him. As one nurse expresses it, the doctor puts the nurse in a "bad position" if he fails to give her orders in how to treat the patient.

Nurse: We don't know how we should handle the patient [if he doesn't give us orders]; what we do might even be the opposite of what we should do. When we should be lenient with a patient, we might be firm. If he doesn't tell us to be firm or lenient with his patient, we may do the reverse of what we should do. It puts the nurse in a bad position.

Interviewer: How do you mean, puts you in a bad position?

Nurse: We don't know if we are doing the right thing. We might even be doing something to hurt the patient. We don't know.

Another nurse expresses these costs in terms of "insecurity."

It makes me insecure with the doctor, as well as with the patient, when I don't know what the doctor's views are and what's going

21. Brown, "Problems of Social Organization . . . ," p. 90.

on with the patient. This makes me insecure because I may be doing something wrong with the patient. A lot of time we need support with a patient, and need to go to him for this.

To prevent this costly situation, the nurse must maintain her relationship with the resident. Her strategies of deference are to be viewed from this perspective. By refusing openly to question the resident's orders, she does not alienate him, thereby *maintaining* her relationship with him; this prevents the cost of "relating to" patients without knowing what to do—that is, without sufficient direction from the resident. Support for this hypothesis is provided by the following data on each of the three power strategies.

One nurse says she goes to the ward chief so she will not "threaten" the resident. If she openly questions his order, he is threatened and becomes angry.

The resident may want to put the patient on sedation. He may be having trouble with the patient and it's extremely easy to give the patient sedation. This way he gets the patient off his back, you see—and maybe he thinks others, too. But the emphasis is on psychotherapy, so the nurse might question this. The doctor will get angry.

She also says that she must have "good interpersonal relationships" with residents so she can talk to them. If she "threatens" them by questioning their order, her relationships with them are strained—"I can't talk to them." Consequently, "I go to the ward chief and tell him what the situation is," rather than questioning the resident's orders.

Another nurse quite explicitly reveals the maintaining and cost-preventing functions of *tertius gaudens*.

Nurse: When there is something in the order that I don't think ought to be, I go to the ward chief. I have been in arguments with residents on this before. When they put something in the nursing care plan that shouldn't be there, the ward chief will take care of it. I don't need to make a big fuss about it. I have gone directly to the resident. I have gone and told him what I thought, but this always would end up in a terrible verbal fight. I don't want to go through that any more. That hasn't happened often, but *it ruins our relationship,* and [in these instances] we had real good relationships, too.

Interviewer: What would a good relationship between you and the resident be like?

Nurse: I would feel comfortable in talking to him about the patient's problems. And he would feel the same way about talking to me. He would listen to me when I have something to say. Most of my relationships with residents are like this. But our relationship was ruined when I went directly to him like this.

In this case we see the close connection between the maintaining and the cost-preventing functions of deference. By going to the ward chief rather than directly to the resident, the nurse maintains a good relationship with the resident—a "comfortable" relationship—in which they discuss the patient's problems. When she questions his orders, however, she is deprived of this relationship and, therefore, the facilities of direction and guidance.

In discussing her reasons for confronting the resident with observations which indicate that some other order is recommended, a nurse reveals the potential strain which exists in the nurse-resident relationship. She also reveals the function performed by the strategy of symbolic *tertius gaudens.* She states that she resorts to this strategy because in past disagreements with the resident:

He would get angry and I would get hostile. *The whole relationship would blow-up*—he would get so mad. It would just be a mess. This hasn't happened since last fall; but when it does, it leads to all sorts of blow-ups.

Another reports the following as reasons for confronting the doctor with a report of the patient's behavior, rather than expressing her opinions to him:

Nurse: Well, I guess a nurse in talking to a doctor has to be a little more diplomatic.

Interviewer: How do you mean, a little more diplomatic?

Nurse: Well, our observations are important, but we can't tell the doctor what to do. We aren't doctors. They are the ones who are supposed to be right, but a lot of times they aren't. But when they are not right, we can't tell them. *It's a matter of interpersonal relations.*

Interviewer: How do you mean?

Nurse: Well, like if I contradict him or let him know that I disagree with him, *he doesn't feel right about it. He doesn't feel comfortable with me and I don't feel comfortable about it either.* He's the doctor and it's his decision to make, not mine. When you tell him, then it's his duty to, well, let you know—he has to take the position that whether you [nurse] like it or not, I am right. He can't let you tell him what to do. If you do, he has to put you in your place and *then your interpersonal relationship with him is destroyed.* I have to be careful not to do this. *The nurse and the doctor have to have a good interpersonal relationship in order to work as a team.*

Regarding the strategy of asking questions, a nurse states that she *could* tell the resident he had given an improper order, but chooses to ask him questions about the patient instead.

I have [told him] a couple of times. It ended up in a mess. It ended up with us in an argument. I don't want to go through that anymore.

By implication, this nurse reveals the maintaining cost-preventing function of the strategy of asking questions. To the extent that the resident and nurse get involved in arguments, they will not likely work effectively in a face-to-face capacity. The fact that she does not want to become implicated in arguments suggests the cost-preventing function of asking questions, although she is not explicit about the nature of the costs. That is, she does not state that arguments with residents result in the cost of having to relate to patients without adequate direction.

The nurse who is "insecure" without the resident's orders is more explicit about the cost-preventing function of asking questions. If she expresses her opinion, the resident

wouldn't like it and this would make me insecure. He would get mad and *wouldn't discuss the patient with me* at all then. It works out better if we just ask him; work around it this way. If I told him [what I thought], it would make me insecure—*I wouldn't be able to find out anything about the patient then.*

Thus, these data reveal that the nurse employs deference to influence the resident because he has power over her as well as authority. Her actions are oriented to the legitimate authority order, but they are also oriented to the power order. To be sure, they cannot be understood except when viewed in terms of their orientation to the normative authority structure, but it is only when the resident's power over her is considered, and its analytic distinction from his authority made explicit, that the function of her power strategies is seen. The involvement of both the residents' authority and power in the nurse's actions is clearly illustrated in the following comment by a head nurse.

> In psychiatry, the nurse often knows much more about psychiatry than the resident. She's had a lot more experience and knows more about psychiatry. . . . She is a nurse and he is a doctor and so he automatically knows more than she does—but sometimes he doesn't. She may know more but she isn't supposed to, and she can't let him know because she isn't supposed to know more than the doctor. Because she does know more than he does, the resident is threatened by her and will reject her. . . . But the nurse and resident must work together if the nurse is to be of much help to the patient.

In light of the above analysis, the difference between implementing strategies and those of the nurse is obvious. The former strategies are cost inducing; the latter are cost preventing. This is not to say that any *concrete* influence attempt must be classified as an implementing *or* maintaining strategy. The same strategy—e.g., *tertius gaudens*—may have a cost-inducing function under some circumstances and a cost-preventing function under other circumstances. In fact, the same strategy (*tertius gaudens*) is shown to have different functions for the recreator and social worker on the one hand, and the nurse on the other. Also, what is primarily an implementing strategy may also perform a maintaining function. For example, the social workers' implementing strategies may be viewed as means of maintaining the social worker-resident relationship. Like the nurses, they utilized forms of deference behavior (e.g., "tact") to influence the resident. The data on social workers were not explicit on this point, but it is reasonable to assume that if the social worker tried to "tell" the resident what he should do, she would alienate him. Therefore, the social worker's implementing strategies may also be viewed as cost preventing: to alienate the resident would place her in the situation of doing less casework treatment, since the resident has the power to prevent her from performing this role. Also, it would probably lead to the resident's withdrawal and avoidance behavior in reference to the social worker-resident collaborative relationship, i.e., he would fail to schedule collaborative conferences with the social worker, thereby depriving her of information needed to perform casework treatment effectively. Hence, maintaining and preventing strategies must be understood in terms of their *analytic* properties: both cost functions may be involved in the same concrete influence attempt.

If an influence attempt may be an implementing strategy under one circumstance and a maintaining strategy under another, it is relevant to ask what this particular circumstance is. Studies of the recreator and social workers suggest that implementing strategies must be exerted in the absence of normative rules binding the actions of others; and that an important structural strategy is the imposition of normative rules on others, putting the relationship on an established basis, and thereby eliminating the costs of implementing strategies. The implication is, then, that the particular circumstance which determines whether a strategy is implementing or maintaining is the degree to which the actors are involved in a relatively well-defined and structured social relationship. Under relatively normless conditions the costly implementing strategies predominate. Rules are then introduced in an effort to reduce costly activity. Once the relationship has been established, influence attempts—to the extent that they are required—become maintaining strategies. Therefore, the particular circumstance under which we would expect the different types of strategies to predominate is the extent to which social relationships are institutionalized.

A comparison of the recreator, social workers, and nurses, in terms of their degree of institutionalization in the Department supports this hypothesis. The analysis of the recreator, we remember, was actually in terms of her attempts to become institutionalized. During the major part of her first year in the Department, she operated without a formal statement of her role. She was new to the Department and had few institutionalized relationships with residents, patients, and nursing personnel. Consequently, she experienced the difficulty of others not responding in accordance with the needs of the recreation program. She also experienced the problem of others *not knowing of the existence* of a recreation service in the Department, as well as having to work fifty-five to sixty hours per week, instead of forty.

Social workers, on the other hand, had been an established fixture of the Department for several years. They did not experience the problem of others not knowing of their existence, nor the problem of having to work additional hours each week to influence others' compliance. Yet, some of the same elements found in the study of the recreator were also found in the study of social workers. There was no formal definition of their role, and evidence indicated that the social workers' casework conception of their role was not congruent with the psychiatrists' conception. Also, social workers experienced the problem of residents not co-operating with them. And, like the recreator, they had to perform cost-inducing power strategies.

The nurses have no problem of their services not being used or of others not knowing of their existence. Also, unlike the members of the other two professions, there *are* formal rules (SOP's) applied to the nurses' activities and to the residents' activity vis-à-vis the nurse. There are the formal order book, regularly scheduled ward rounds and team meetings, as well as face-to-face contact and discussions throughout the day in which the doctor instructs the nurse in how she should "relate to" patients.

The nurses' problem does not stem from a lack of institutionalization—residents' refusing to provide them with facilities (orders)—but from a conflict between two institutionalized orders: conflict between the moral obligation for the patient's welfare and the responsibility to obey the doctor's order. Most nurses attempt to resolve this conflict by trying to influence the doctor's order through deference, which also functions to maintain the relational system and prevent costs. We argue that these strategies, because of their emphasis on maintaining the relational system, characterize social relationships which have attained a high degree of institutionalization. The theory is that cost-inducing implementing strategies predominate under conditions of minimum institutionalization, where relationships are ambiguously and vaguely defined. Rules and norms are then introduced, clarifying the relationship. Such structural strategies cut costs and stabilize (institutionalize) the relationship. Then if power strategies are necessary, they perform the functions of maintaining the relationship and preventing costs.

SUMMARY AND CONCLUSIONS

Examination of the nurses' reaction to a role conflict reveals their use of three types of power strategies in their attempts to influence the residents. All strategies have in common the fact that each is designed to maintain the resident-nurse relationship and so to prevent costs for the nurse. On this basis, the concept of maintaining cost-preventing power strategy was derived.

Differences between nurses, social workers, and the recreator in terms of their relationship with residents suggest that the power strategy scheme is related to the institutionalization process. It is hypothesized that the occurrence of each type of power strategy (implementing cost-inducing, structural cost-reducing, and maintaining cost-preventing) is related to the degree to which the actor-other relationship is institutionalized.

PART III

EXPRESSIVE
ORIENTATIONS

8 THE RECREATOR: CONFLICT BETWEEN INSTRUMENTAL AND EXPRESSIVE ORIENTATIONS

Heretofore, we have been exclusively concerned with an actor's instrumental orientations and the processes involved in obtaining *facilities* from others. We will now turn our attention to expressive orientations and the actor's problem of eliciting *rewards* (favorable attitudes) from others. Our general objective is to ascertain whether the problem of eliciting rewards is essentially different from the problem of eliciting facilities.

The present chapter deals with the recreator and revolves around her desire for recognition as one who makes a unique and valuable contribution to patient treatment. We recall her problem of getting others to respond according to the needs of her instrumental role. In addition, she has a problem of rewards —getting others to recognize recreation as an important aspect of psychiatric treatment. A first indication of this is her desire for recreation to be seen as a separate and autonomous service from occupational therapy.

It should be noted first that the recreation service and occupational therapy are, formally, two separate units. Each service has a separate budgeted position in the Department, as well as separate offices, schedule of patient activities, and supplies and equipment. The two services obtain independent referrals from the doctors, which are also different in nature: the occupational therapy referrals are by prescription or order from the doctor, while the recreation "referrals" are not. Objectively, then, the two services are structurally differentiated units of the Department.

Nevertheless, the recreator complains that Department personnel "are always confusing occupational therapy with recreation," and that she is "continually having to correct people." Recreation is a separate service, but others do not recognize it as such. For example, once during ward rounds a nurse referred to the multi-purpose room as the occupational therapy area, whereupon the recreator informed her that this was "the occupational therapy *and* recreation area." The recreator states that, although this "doesn't appear to be important," she must correct people because she has "to let them know" that she too has "something to contribute to patients."

Ways of impressing her separate identity on organizational personnel are not limited to such explicit techniques. Nurses, for example, are used to obtain recognition from residents. When nurses accompany patients to recreation activities, the recreator asks them to report in nurses' notes—which are read daily by the charge nurse during ward rounds—something that a patient did in recreation. Also, for ward rounds and team meetings which she misses, she asks nurses to mention these things in person. She feels that "When you are new, you have to do these things. If you don't, well, take resident _____ this morning. He confused the square dance [a recreation activity] with occupational therapy." The resident had made reference to the week-end square dance for patients in occupational therapy.

The recreator does not want recognition for recognition's sake, however. She wants recognition as a person who has a professional contribution to make to patient treatment. She manifests this need also in reference to her relation to occupational therapy. She feels that "an inexperienced person" would have sought an opportunity to have a conflict with occupational therapy in order "to get recognition." However, since she feels that she is experienced in her profession and has "learned professional responsibility," and because of the "professional pride involved," she has been cautious not to have a conflict with the other service, as this would have reflected a lack of professional responsibility. Consequently, she has tried to get recognition by making a "positive contribution."

Recreation services, like all other services for patients, can be considered of value—to make a "positive contribution" —only in terms of their ability to meet patients' needs. Since doctors decide what these needs are and therefore what is of value to patients, their use of "ancillary" services should be important to members of an "ancillary" service. Consequently, doctors are an important reference group which the recreator uses to make evaluations of herself and her work. The important question then becomes, what are the precise reference points through which the recreator does this? That is, what are the particular kinds of activity on the part of the physician which are the basis for the recreator's evaluation of herself? True, it is in reference to his use of her services, but it is the particular manner in which he uses them. Events surrounding the recreator's orientation session with residents[1] illuminate the manner in which her services must be used before the recreator feels her services are highly regarded.

The orientation session was the first the recreator had with the residents, and it had been arranged by the senior psychiatrists on the inpatient service. Rather than asking for the session, the recreator *purposely* waited until psychiatrists asked her to conduct it. She realizes "it took longer that way," but she feels she "gained more." She gained more because

> it's like being asked for, rather than having to ask. They ask something from me, not my asking to give something to them. . . . *It's a sign of their respect for what I can contribute. A recognition of its value.*

Thus, for psychiatrists to ask her to do this symbolizes their respect for her work. To be asked is rewarding since it conveys a high regard for her—recognition of the value of recreation services. This suggests, then, that it is through their *voluntary* use of recreation services that doctors convey a high evaluation of the recreator.

Additional support for this is indicated from the orientation session itself. In this session, which was fifteen minutes late starting because all residents were late, the recreator was scheduled

1. See pp. 37-38 above.

to talk for two hours, but spoke for only forty-five minutes because she felt the residents were not interested. Immediately following her lecture she asked for a question and answer period, to be met by an interval of silence. Finally, two residents asked questions. One wanted to know about the differences between occupational therapy and recreation and if the recreator had any conflict with occupational therapy personnel; the other asked if the recreator wanted a referral form on every patient.

Immediately following the session the recreator stated, "That was the most painful experience I have ever had." Upon being asked what she meant, she replied: "Their attitude. They may as well have not even been here. They weren't the least bit interested. They were only here because they had to be." The recreator wanted residents to attend because they were interested in recreation services and recognized their importance in the treatment of patients, not because they *had* to attend. She wanted them to attend voluntarily. She wanted them to indicate their interest and to accept what she had to say as something of value. However, "They were all late. . . . They didn't accept anything I said. . . . There was just a lack of interest. . . . Just no acceptance."

The two examples above surrounding the orientation session are not specifically concerned with the doctor's use of recreation services, since neither has to do with referrals. However, they indicate to the recreator something of the attitude of respect (or disrespect) doctors have for recreation services. Also, since respect is conveyed through the voluntary use of recreation services, the implication is that certain methods of getting referrals (facilities) may get the recreator little respect. This is so because, in her influence attempts, referrals originate with the recreator and not the doctor; the doctor is coerced into making referrals, rather than making them voluntarily. That certain strategies may facilitate instrumental orientations but not expressive orientations is illustrated by the recreator's comments on the use of the chief resident to help her get referrals.

> I don't like to do that, you know. That way I feel it's all this way (moves her arm up and down). It's a line of authority—the resident is doing it because he is told to do so.

Through *tertius gaudens* the recreator can attempt to get the *facility* of referral. The same strategy cannot get her the *reward-*

ing attitudes of respect and recognition due one who performs valuable work, however, for residents express these attitudes only when they voluntarily send her referrals. The doctor has to want her services—to indicate that he has a need for them—before she can feel he evaluates her as someone who performs a "positive contribution."

This is not to suggest that instrumental and expressive orientations are inherently incompatible. It can be seen, for example, that if the referral form which the recreator introduced had been accepted and used voluntarily,[2] it would have symbolized the residents' respect for recreation services—recognition of the importance and value her services have for psychiatric patients. Therefore, the referral form would have served both an instrumental and expressive purpose. In addition, attending ward rounds and team meetings is a way of letting residents know she is "around" (i.e., a way to get recognition), as well as to elicit specific referrals.

Nevertheless, there seems to be a particular problem involved in expressive orientations that is not encountered in instrumental orientations. In the former, the actor is concerned with the other's attitudinal evaluation of him. In the latter, he is more concerned with the other simply co-operating with him—helping him perform a task, with no particular concern with what the other thinks about him so long as he co-operates. Even if the other does not want to co-operate, strategies may be employed to make him co-operative, e.g., *tertius gaudens*. When *both* instrumental and expressive responses are desired from a specific other, it may be possible to obtain the former but not the latter. In the case of the orientation session, for example, the recreator had the authority and positive sanctions of the psychiatrists to have the session—"They thought it was important to have me do this," but the residents "don't have to accept it." As she says, she "can't make them accept it" or "shove it down their throats." Similarly, for *tertius gaudens* to obtain referrals: she can "motivate" residents to give her referrals, but it is something else for them to use recreation services voluntarily.

This is not to say that in relatively exclusive instrumental relationships the actor will be unconcerned about others' attitudes toward him. The recreator's comments about the nursing per-

2. As previously noted, residents never accepted the referral form.

sonnel indicate otherwise.[3] In that case, however, concern was not so much with the nurses' evaluation of her, but with their acceptance of what she did so that she could turn her back. Nurses were primarily important in terms of their cost-reducing functions for her instrumental, rather than expressive, orientations.

Although the recreator needs to coerce residents to comply in accordance with her instrumental considerations, she has a need not to coerce deriving from her expressive orientations. This conflict, incidentally, is not unlike the "approach-avoidance" form of psychological conflict. As interpreted in this study, it is conflict which—while having its psychological elements—is not understandable until viewed in terms of certain social properties possessed by residents as significant others. Residents possess two different values for the recreator: the instrumental *facility* of referrals and the expressive *reward* of respecting and appreciating her work. The conflict derives from the instrumental necessity of referrals and the expressive costs of exerting influence to obtain them.

On the basis of these considerations, it is suggested that the problem of eliciting rewards to facilitate expressive orientations poses a more difficult problem than does the problem of eliciting facilities alone. The former requires that the other hold evaluative attitudes (therefore, "internal states") toward the actor that are positive in nature (respectful, appreciative, etc.), *in addition* to providing him with a purely instrumental and co-operative act. For example, the recreator wanted residents to use her services and attend the orientation session because they recognized the value of recreation services, not because they had to or because they were told to use them. This has further implications regarding the institutionalization process. If ego wants expressive responses from others, institutionalizing their responses may reduce his costly instrumental activities without reducing costs associated with expressive deprivation. Others' responses may be due to formal SOP's and routine rules and not their respect and appreciation of the actor and his work. If the recreator had been successful in getting the referral form accepted, for example, referrals might have become merely a matter of routine.

Finally, the analysis of the recreator illustrates the importance of evaluative reference groups and the need to distinguish these

3. See pp. 54-55 above.

from normative and comparative reference groups. A normative reference group provides the actor with norms which he assimilates, becoming bases for his attitudes. An example of this in the case of the recreator is the principle of spontaneity in recreation activities which derives from the profession of recreation. A comparative reference group, on the other hand, is a group which the individual "uses as a reference point in making evaluations of himself or others." [4] In the case of the recreator, occupational therapy as a comparative reference group is implied in the recreator's move to institutionalize the referral procedure. She states that occupational therapy has a referral procedure; therefore, "we want one, too."

Note that a comparative reference group functions as a reference point in order to make an evaluation of oneself; it is *not* necessarily the group that conveys the evaluation. That is to say, evaluative reference groups are sources of the *reward* of positive evaluation, whereas comparative reference groups function as standards whereby one evaluates whether he is getting the reward and to what extent he is getting it. Although it is clear that psychiatrists are an important evaluative reference group, data are less clear regarding the group(s) which function as reference points for the recreator to assess whether or not she receives a high or low evaluation from psychiatrists.

To make more concrete the distinction between comparative and evaluative reference groups, an example will be given which may not be completely valid. It was shown that psychiatrists are an important evaluative reference group for the recreator and that they convey a high evaluation of her services when they use them voluntarily. However, it may be that the voluntary use of her service is indicative of a high evaluation of her service (i.e., a "recognition of its value") because this is the way psychiatrists use other "ancillary" services (e.g., occupational therapy). If this is the case, other "ancillary" services might function as comparative reference groups which provide the standards (i.e., "reference points") through which the evaluation is conveyed and received.

4. Harold H. Kelley, "Two Functions of Reference Groups," in Guy E. Swanson, Theodore M. Newcomb, and Eugene L. Hartley, *Readings in Social Psychology* (2nd ed.; New York: Henry Holt and Company, 1952), p. 412.

SUMMARY AND CONCLUSIONS

To become institutionalized into the Department, the recreator had not only a problem of eliciting instrumental responses from others, but also the problem of receiving positive expressive responses. Evidence indicates that the problem of obtaining these two types of responses differs in important ways. Expressive responses (rewards) refer to other's attitudes toward the actor and are more difficult to influence and manipulate than his overt instrumental acts. It may be possible, therefore, to influence his instrumental response without influencing his expressive response. Within the context of the institutionalization process, the problem may be one in which other's instrumental acts become institutionalized through the application of normative rules, but where his expressive responses—which may be equally important to the actor—have not been so institutionalized. In this event, the actor may be able to cut excessive costs involved in the instrumental performance of his role, but continue to experience the deprivation of expressive costs. Institutionalizing expressive responses is a problem which must be solved in addition to institutionalizing instrumental responses.

Finally, data indicate the presence of an "evaluative other" in expressive orientations and, therefore, suggest the empirical relevance of the evaluative reference group formulation.

9 THE PSYCHOLOGIST'S TEST REPORT: BUREAUCRACY AND THE PROBLEM OF EXPRESSIVE GRATIFICATION

In this chapter we will explore further the problem outlined in the preceding chapter: the problem of incompatibility between the actor's instrumental and expressive orientations, particularly in reference to the institutionalization of the other's response. Analysis will be in terms of the psychologist's verbal reporting of his test results, with specific attention focused on the psychologist's perception of the psychiatrist's respect (or disrespect) for his report. The social worker's observation that social workers are more dependent on the psychiatrists and have to work closer with them than do psychologists[1] is certainly borne out by the analysis of the psychologist's diagnostic role in Chapter 6; her statement that psychologists do not care what psychiatrists do with testing results once they have been reported is subject to question, however. It is this question that we investigate in this chapter.

1. See p. 77 above.

The procedure used for the verbal reporting of psychological test data varies from service to service. On the inpatient service, there is no formal procedure for test reporting. If the psychologist considers the results important, he may volunteer the information during ward rounds; also, the attending man may occasionally ask for a verbal report. On the outpatient service, the psychologist regularly gives his report during the diagnostic conference; the conference is attended by a resident, a staff psychiatrist who chairs the conference, a psychologist, and sometimes a social worker. On the basis of the information presented by the therapist, psychologist, and social worker, a diagnosis is made. Essentially the same situation prevails in the child service, except the psychologist's report is based on battery tests rather than the MMPI and sentence completion tests.

Psychologists report no difficulties in not being able to give their report. However, psychologists from all three services claim there is a lack of "respect," "appreciation," and "acceptance" accorded their test data.

On the inpatient service, for example, one mentions that test data are accepted and used only when they confirm the psychiatrist's own judgment. "If the test doesn't agree with their own judgment, they tend not to accept the test." This psychologist "would like to see greater professional respect for the psychologists, greater appreciation of our competence, of our usefulness, on the part of the psychiatric staff." Another also mentions the tendency for test data to be accepted only when they are confirming: "Validation data are always a welcome sign, especially when it comes to diagnosis," but "it's not all right when he ignores data when they contradict what he thinks about the case." Another inpatient psychologist states:

> Specific psychiatrists I detest working with. A few will have nothing to do with the psychologist's data at all. They pay absolutely no attention to his report, verbal or written. There's one fellow whose typical pattern of interacting with psychologists is particularly frustrating. You will present something in rounds and his reaction is a bit irritating. You will say what you find. This will almost inevitably be different from what he has said, and he will interrupt you. What he is trying to do is wind up saying that he knew all about it; acting like you didn't tell him anything he didn't already know. He'll be sitting there observably nodding his head every time you say something. It's kind of frustrating to

work with a person like this. You know you are making a contribution and he's using it, but [he] won't accept you as an independent professional with your own knowledge.

Finally, one inpatient psychologist speaks of the resident who "never listens to the psychologist's verbal report in rounds" and "who never uses test data at all, just ignores them. This is not a real trouble, but it makes the psychologists uncomfortable."

Interviewer: How do you mean?

Psychologist: Well, the psychologist is probably disposed to think his testing data have higher priority than they really have for one thing, I guess. When they are not valued at all, it indicates that they [residents] don't think they are very important. Their value is limited, but I don't think they should be completely ignored if they are going to take up all this time. Different attending men have different attitudes toward psychologists and psychologicals. Some will not show much respect for what he has to say in his report.

Psychologists on the outpatient service always verbally report their testing results. According to one psychologist who has worked on both inpatient and outpatient services, this aspect of the outpatient service has been an important source of satisfaction to him.

The most gratifying experience I have had here was on outpatient where I could offer my opinions and report in case conferences. I have had the feeling that I was contributing something.

Such satisfaction varied, however, depending upon the conference chairman: some failed to see the importance of the psychologist's report. This was especially true for one psychiatrist: "He didn't see that our reports were very important. He wasn't too enthusiastic or interested." Another psychologist who has worked on both services voices the same general dissatisfactions, but feels that testing results are appreciated more on the inpatient service than on the outpatient service.

Psychologist: There's no trouble with residents on the inpatient service. I have felt all along that I was helping them. I get feedback from them. On outpatient, I don't feel what I'm doing is important. Testing results aren't used as much. In fact they tend to be ignored by some.

Interviewer: This is on the outpatient?

Psychologist: Yeah, not the inpatient. It depends on the resident. Some residents seem to think we are more or less technicians—someone to do a routine service. I don't feel motivated to give a good report under these conditions. Some of them don't think it's very important. So if he feels it's a garbage report, I'll give him a garbage report. It won't be garbage, but it won't be as good a report as otherwise. On the inpatient, I have felt most motivated. I've felt that tests were appreciated and that it did something, that it made a contribution. I've gotten feedback from them, but never from the outpatient service.

Interviewer: How do you mean feedback?

Psychologist: They'll see me and say that the report is good, that it pointed out something that they weren't aware of. Or they might ask me how I knew this, and I could explain it to them. Things like this indicate that they have some value for what I'm doing; they realize its contribution. A lot of them think that they don't offer anything and would rather not be bothered with them.

No more explicit statement is needed to illustrate the point that motivation to participate in an organization (to remain in the organization) is not necessarily accompanied by motivation to produce.[2] In addition to providing sufficient satisfaction for the individual to become a member, the organization must motivate him to produce. And it is through the gratification of his expressive orientations that this psychologist is motivated to produce. He wants residents to indicate a value for his work by telling him his report is good, to let him know that he reveals things about patients they are unable to find, and to give him the opportunity to explain how he is able to discover things with his tests. In short, he wants professional respect. Otherwise, he gives "garbage reports."

Another outpatient psychologist, in commenting on the "occasional ignoring" of test data, feels that when test data are ignored, "the optimum decision for a particular patient isn't likely to be made." However,

Probably more important maybe is that, when they ignore what I say, it sets up personal feelings because a great amount of work

2. On this point, see James G. March and Herbert A. Simon, *Organizations* (New York: John Wiley and Sons, Inc., 1958), pp. 34-81, 83-111.

is ignored. If I put my time on these tests, I expect my opinions to be *respected* and taken for what they are.

Finally, another outpatient psychologist states:

> I'm somewhat dissatisfied with the attitude of some of the senior staff toward psychological tests. Some of them don't seem to think they are of much, if any, value. Residents don't feel this way, only the senior staff. But the attitude is catching. What we do should be *appreciated,* but some of the staff don't. This, of course, is partly due to the fact that we almost exclusively use routine tests, but they do have a contribution and this *should be recognized.* They may be routine but a lot of time and effort goes into them, and this should be *appreciated* more.

> Interviewer: It seems, then, that you are saying the problem is not with the fact that you are prevented from performing your diagnostic service, but a matter of the way it is accepted.

> Psychologist: No, it's not a problem of their [tests] not being done. It's just the attitude of the psychiatrists toward what we do—the attitude of not thinking it's important. It's this attitude that's particularly griping.

A psychologist who has worked on all three services thinks the psychologist's report is respected more on the child service. This stems from the fact that more powerful tests are used and the patients are children.

> Psychologist: The service on outpatient and inpatient is much more limited in value. The psychiatrist knows it and the psychologist knows it. The value just isn't there, so the psychiatrists are not as willing to accept it or pay as much attention to it.

> Interviewer: Seems you are saying that the psychiatrists are justified in seeing a limited value in it.

> Psychologist: Yeah. But not as much as some like to admit. It [test] doesn't tell much. We know that as well as they do. But it tells more than some of them will admit.

While this problem is not as great on the child service, it still exists.

> Psychologist: [On the child service] the psychologist is looked to for information a little more, his opinion counts more, the tests are valued more than on the other services. But here it will

depend on the psychiatrist. With some it will be difficult to get along with. Some psychiatrists don't have good working relationships with psychologists. I can't work with some psychiatrists at all.

Interviewer: What would the psychiatrist do to create this kind of situation?

Psychologist: Generally snubbing you—not paying any attention to your report, ignoring it. Some will demand a lot of work —you will give a fairly extensive battery of tests—and he won't appreciate it. . . . Taking what you say and twisting it—reinterpreting what you have said. I know my tests and how to interpret them; I don't like him twisting what I say like this. What gripes us more than anything is his acceptance of what we say if it agrees with what he says. If he doesn't, he will ignore it. This isn't the usual thing. All of them aren't like this—only a few.

Two other psychologists on the child service voice the same general complaints as do those on the other services. One feels that "complaint" is too strong a word, however, stating that although test data are sometimes "pretty much disregarded, this isn't the rule by any means."

In my experience I think this has happened only a very few times. But a number of students do feel that psychologists' findings could be used more by the child's therapist.

The other mentions the problem of psychiatrists' not thinking the psychologist's work is as important and ignoring his opinion.

Everyone likes to feel that one's work is important, and many residents feel our work is important. All people want to feel this; no one likes to feel that his work is unimportant. There are some residents who seem not to think it's important. I think a lot of dissatisfaction on the part of psychologists stems from this. Some of the staff seem to take the attitude that we are professional hired help, and don't seem willing to treat us like full-fledged professional people. . . . Sometimes our opinions will be ignored in diagnostic conferences. I don't mind if they disagree with me, but I don't like to be not listened to and have my professional opinion ignored. None of us likes this.

The above data have been presented in rather complete detail because of the crucial role they play in throwing light on a complex theoretical problem. In the first instance, they point to a subtle difference between the gratification of instrumental and expressive orientations. In terms of instrumental considerations —the actual work involved in his diagnostic function—the psychologist experiences little difficulty. With the few exceptions of battery testing, no problems are experienced in receiving referrals, administering tests, and reporting test results.[3] The psychologist, unlike the recreator and social worker, must rarely exert extra effort and other costly activity to get residents to comply with actions (facilities) that are necessary for his own role performance. As was pointed out in Chapter 6, this is due to certain structural, bureaucratic mechanisms which mediate between the psychologist and the resident. In terms of expressive orientations—which are dependent on others' expressions of respect, appreciation, and acceptance—we find a different picture: psychologists report a lack of appreciation, respect, acceptance, and recognition for their test data by either staff psychiatrists or residents, or both. To be sure, this complaint is often made of only a few psychiatrists or residents. Nevertheless, the problem is serious enough for psychologists to volunteer these responses while discussing their diagnostic function or in reply to a very much open-ended question.[4]

These findings are consistent with those of the preceding chapter. They too point to differences in the nature of the other's responses needed to facilitate one's instrumental orientations on the one hand and expressive orientations on the other, and the implications these differences have for the process of institutionalization. Although instrumental responses from psychiatrists are institutionalized by certain bureaucratic routines and standard operating procedures, expressive responses are not. The overt instrumental act (facility) may be institutionalized, but the internal attitude (reward) of respect and appreciation may not. Institutionalizing expressive responses, therefore, should be viewed as a problem to be solved *in addition* to the institutionalization of instrumental responses. Social rules and norms may coerce others to comply with the instrumental needs of an actor, but they may

3. Except for receiving referrals on the one ward which houses severely disturbed patients. See p. 87 above.
4. The question was, "Do you have any trouble, problems, or difficulties with anyone during diagnostic conferences (or ward rounds)?" Only two psychologists failed to mention the above complaints, and one of these subsequently did so in reply to the question: "How much do you feel the psychological test data are used by psychiatrists?"

not result in expressions of respect and appreciation for him.

An example will put this phenomenon in clear perspective. It is formal SOP for the outpatient psychologist to make a verbal report of his test data during the outpatient diagnostic conference. The psychiatrist's overt behavior is institutionalized, in the sense that he must ask the psychologist to give his report. This does not mean, however, that the psychiatrist must show respect for the psychologist's report; the psychiatrist's overt act may be institutionalized and become a function of social norms (SOP's), but his attitude toward the psychologist may not. This duality between the overt act and the internal attitude can be readily gleaned from the following remarks of a psychiatric resident. This resident does not "consider [psychological tests] of much value because of their lack of validity and [his] own personal bias"; but because he has no choice in the matter, he routinely refers each of his patients for psychological testing. He often ignores the psychologist's report, however.

> I have to admit that I don't have any difficulty with the psychologist as a person. But I don't have much faith in his psychological data, as opposed to clinical data. It seems that it is only useful for confirmation. When we are far apart [in our reports] I will tend to disregard his data. I'm sure [his data] does have some validity. However, while a one-hour interview with the patient is not much, I do get distinct impressions; and if psychological data disagree with my impressions, I tend to ignore them. My feeling is that psychological tests are an ancillary aid only, and you cannot evaluate persons cold like this with no personal relationship. I feel that in many cases they are just confirming the clinical material I have already given. I'm not saying they are doing this intentionally. But I can't understand why they are even given. I know for a fact that the staff men don't value them, but they always ask them to give their report. I can't understand why; but they always ask them to give their report. I can't understand why; I know they don't value them unless they are confirming. But if they are in disagreement, they tend to ignore them, too.

Bureaucratic routine requires that the psychologist be permitted to report his test data. It cannot, however, prevent the psychiatrist (staff or resident) from ignoring them and refusing to express a value for them. The test referral is a matter of bureaucratic routine and *not* a decision by the psychiatrist, based on the needs of his patient. Consequently, test referrals are not expressions of value for the psychologist and his test data—referrals are made *whether they are needed or not.* A psychologist puts the point this way.

> My biggest complaint is the prevailing attitude of the psychiatrists that psychology is an ancillary profession. They seem to think we are some sort of technician performing something like a urinalysis for them. Whenever they want a testing done, they just order it like they do a urinalysis. Their attitude toward us is about the same as it is toward someone doing a urinalysis. It's not all their fault. We've brought it on ourselves by doing it. We shouldn't have ever started giving tests like this [MMPI and sentence completion] in the first place. *A lot of them don't even want tests—it's just a routine thing that is done.*

Other data throw further light on the relative differences between instrumental and expressive deprivation. It will be recalled that when psychologists experience difficulty obtaining appropriate instrumental responses from residents, e.g., getting a vague referral, they report doing something about it, e.g., chasing the residents down.[5] In contrast, the following are what psychologists report doing when residents or psychiatrists ignore and fail to listen to their reports, or generally fail to respect them.

> If he doesn't want to listen to test data, *there's nothing I can do.*

> If the resident doesn't listen to the psychologist's report, *I don't know what one can do about it.*

> [There is] not much you can do other than do your best. Then if they still don't appreciate it, that's it. *It's up to them. You can't make a campaign and try to get them to recognize their importance and appreciate the contribution of them.*

> [I cannot do anything] other than demonstrate my competence from day to day. *There's nothing you can do more than this.* If they don't recognize my competence, I can't do anything.

These comments suggest that although it is possible to coerce facilities, or overt acts, it may not be possible to coerce rewards. Others' attitudes are more difficult to manipulate than their overt instrumental acts; consequently, it is harder to "make" others appreciate you than it is to co-operate with you.

5. See pp. 87-89 above.

This generalization requires a qualification. It is true that one cannot coerce another to change his attitudes; nevertheless, it is possible to try to influence a change in these attitudes. Psychologists have indicated a desire for psychiatrists to express an attitude of respect for their work. Such respect depends upon psychiatrists seeing a value in the psychologists' work. Therefore, psychologists must demonstrate the value of their work to psychiatrists. To do this, psychologists must work hard and do their work competently. Then, if there is no change in the psychiatrists' attitude, there is little that psychologists can do. As one of the above respondents states, there's "not much you can do other than do your best. Then, if they still don't appreciate it, that's it. It's up to them."

When it is realized that doing one's best may be viewed as an influence attempt to bring about a change in the attitudes of others, important implications for the organizational allocation of rewards appear. If organizational effectiveness is dependent on the motivation of members to produce, the optimum condition of effectiveness will be at some point *short* of maximum expressive gratification for organizational participants; it is only under such conditions that they will be motivated to do their best in order to get appreciative responses from significant others.[6] Expressive deprivation should not be too great, however; otherwise, the member may cease to be motivated, as is the case with the psychologist who gives "garbage reports." Or, if he is given the opportunity, the member may "punish" others who fail to show him respect. Three psychologists who complain about sometimes receiving battery test referrals on too short notice say they usually refuse the referral. "When I get a last minute referral, I won't take it. If it's an emergency, I don't see why we can't take it then; in these situations I will take it. But I think we are justifiably angry when they come in at the last minute [unless it's an emergency]."

It is significant to note that when the referring party has no control over the timing of referrals—in emergencies, his attitude toward the psychologist is not subject to scrutiny. When he does have such control, however, his attitudes are scrutinized. For then a "last minute referral" reflects and symbolizes the referring

6. This generalization assumes that there is a "significant other" in the organization from whom the actor wants respectful, appreciative, and accepting responses. This is sometimes not the case.

party's attitude toward the psychologist and his work. That is what makes the above respondent "angry." Although anger is the most immediate response, the respondent reveals an additional response while discussing psychiatrists' lack of respect for his work.

> This is what's involved in the five minute referrals. We feel it's more a matter of their thinking our work is not important to fail to let us know beforehand—that it is some routing thing that can be done on a moment's notice—than it is anything else. It's that more than anything that irritates us. We feel that our work is important, that we deserve a certain amount of professional respect. When they give us referrals like this, we feel it's a professional insult, a lack of professional respect for us, that they think our work is not important. When they do this, we don't accept the referral; I just say I'm all tied up.

The following generalizations are implied. It is under conditions of expressive deprivation that the organizational member will most likely be motivated to produce—that he will be most likely to do his best—in order to influence the attitudes and opinions of significant others toward him and, thereby, obtain better rewards. When expressive deprivation reaches a certain point, however, the member ceases to be motivated. He may become angry and intentionally refuse to co-operate, sabotaging the work of others who fail to reward him.

SUMMARY AND CONCLUSIONS

In Chapter 6 it was shown that psychologists encounter few difficulties obtaining necessary facilities from psychiatrists in their diagnostic role performance. Unlike the recreator and social workers, they have no problem of psychiatrists' failing to use their services and they must rarely exert cost-inducing activities to influence residents to provide them with the appropriate facilities (referrals). Because the physician's activity has been institutionalized by a set of organizational rules, most costs have been structured out of the psychologist-psychiatrist relationship (at least from the psychologist's standpoint).

In this chapter, however, psychologists indicate that their reports are not always accepted and appreciated. Although there is little instrumental deprivation and cost-inducing activity, psychologists report that certain psychiatrists have a low evaluation of them. This finding provides further insight into the problem concerning the relative differences between instrumental and expressive problems. In relation to the process of institutionalization, it suggests that the bureaucratization or institutionalization of expressive responses is a problem which must be solved in addition to the institutionalization of the instrumental facilities. Actors may be coerced by social rules to perform certain instrumental acts and may come to perform them as a matter of routine, without adopting an attitude of respect and appreciation for others.

Data also suggest that, in terms of the actor's influence attempts, the actor is less able to influence the other's evaluative attitudes (rewards) of him than he is to influence the other's instrumental acts (facilities).

10 SOCIAL WORK:

EXPRESSIVE ORIENTATIONS

AND THE PROBLEM

OF PRESTIGE

In this chapter we shall further explore the problem of expressive orientations and deprivation. In the last two chapters we suggested that the institutionalization of expressive responses is a problem which must be solved in addition to the institutionalization of instrumental responses. And we suggested in the preceding chapter that an actor's reaction to expressive deprivation differs from his reaction to instrumental deprivation. Both of these problems will receive a more thorough analysis in the present chapter. In addition to the concept of expressive deprivation, comparative and evaluative reference groups will be the major concepts used.

These problems will be analyzed in terms of the social workers' problems of academic status in the School of Medicine, salary, "professional status," and inadequate and unclear administrative channels—all of which are part of the same basic complex, the problem of prestige or "professional respect." In addition, the functions of social work leadership will be analyzed in reference to this problem. The general problem is to understand why "there is a great need for social workers to scream for status," as one social work supervisor put it.

Requests for academic rank[1] along with higher salaries were voiced on several occasions during the committee meetings between social workers and psychiatrists. In interviews, social work supervisors—the psychiatric social work supervisor and the overall hospital supervisor of social work—also stated that these two things had been, and continue to be, constant sources of the group's dissatisfactions. Major attention will be devoted to the request for faculty status.

FACULTY STATUS AND SALARY

To understand what is involved in the requests for academic rank, as well as salary increases, the nature of prestige must be understood. Prestige has been defined as a "sentiment in the minds of men that is expressed in interpersonal interaction," the core sentiment being an attitude of respect.[2] Hence, the prestige of one person is dependent on others' expressing respect for him. Since attitudes and sentiments are "inner states," prestige must be "expressed by *marks* of respect from those with whom (one) interacts." [3] The analysis of the request for academic status must begin by viewing such rank as a symbol or mark of prestige.[4] With this in mind, three factors bearing on the request will be considered.

First, one might argue that social workers feel that they have teaching responsibilities and should, therefore, be rewarded with academic rank. There is the objective fact, however, that no so-

1. At this time—that is, at the time of this request—two psychiatric social workers, one of whom is the supervisor, actually had academic status in the School of Medicine.
2. Joseph A. Kahl, *The American Class Structure* (New York: Rinehart and Company, Inc., 1953), p. 8.
3. Harry M. Johnson, *Sociology: A Systematic Introduction* (New York: Harcourt, Brace and Company, 1960), p. 19; emphasis supplied.
4. In the sociological literature, the concept of status is sometimes used to refer to what is here defined as prestige. Since status is most often used to refer to the rights, duties, responsibilities, and privileges surrounding a position in a social structure, prestige is the term used in this study. Social workers and other organizational participants often speak of status rather than prestige, so whenever the former concept appears, it will be written "status."

cial worker carries teaching responsibility in any formal sense;[5] none carries a teaching "load." Indeed, one of the supervisors[6] states that, since social workers do not carry teaching responsibility, they do not have a "leg to stand on as far as academic status is concerned."

A second explanation for the request might be that social workers want to teach medical students, either because there is intrinsic enjoyment to it (or they think there would be), or because of the possible "prestige by association" from "rubbing shoulders" with, and teaching, medical students. The latter explanation is especially appealing in light of the medical profession's high prestige in American society.[7] Nevertheless, social workers give no indication that they *want* to teach medical students, or that they enjoy what teaching they do. They complain that medical students give them a "hard time"; and one supervisor states that social workers do not like to perform this function: social workers are trained to perform a treatment function rather than an educational function, and so do not feel competent in this role. As a result, they "shy away from it." Despite the supervisor's efforts to motivate them, they have not been "too receptive."

Third, social workers are not very clear or decisive in their demands for faculty status. During the first airing of the issue in the committee meetings, this request (along with complaints about salary) was briefly discussed. A social worker then stated that what they were discussing were only "manifestations of what is going on under the surface"—the problem of not being "accepted as a colleague." A later discussion of faculty status prompted the comment from a psychiatrist that "all this business about faculty status doesn't add up." In a still later discussion, another social worker stated that faculty status is not the real problem; lack of

5. A qualification is in order in the case of the psychiatric social work supervisor who had minimum teaching responsibility for medical students. As was noted above, the supervisor had academic rank.
6. To preserve the anonymity of the psychiatric social work supervisor and the over-all hospital supervisor of social work, when reference is made to either of them, they will not be specifically identified except when it is unavoidable.
7. See, for example, Cecil C. North and Paul K. Hatt, "Jobs and Occupations: A Popular Evaluation," in Reinhard Bendix and Seymour M. Lipset (eds.), *Class, Status, and Power* (Glencoe: The Free Press, 1953), pp. 411-36.

"channels to the administration to work on our problems" is what it all "boils down to." Finally, one of the psychiatrists stated he had gotten "the feeling that there is some feeling about it," but he is "not sure how you [social workers] feel about it." The social workers replied that they, too, were not sure about it, nor who among them should have it. One of them stated, "I think this is an area that should be put down for further clarification."

In light of these facts, it does seem that the request for academic status "doesn't add up." It "adds up" only when academic status is viewed as a symbol of prestige; as the one social worker puts it, it's a "manifestation" of something else.

Further insight into this problem is provided by both supervisors who state that the request is very much due to the privileges (e.g., vacation) that go with faculty status. In addition, two social workers take a similar view when interviewed, stating it is a matter of vacation and the pay scale they are on. Still, it is not these things in themselves, but what they *reflect*.

> The social workers only get three weeks' vacation. We get the same as secretaries, janitors, and everybody else employed in the hospital, but not like faculty status.

Not having faculty vacation privileges is important because it symbolizes something about the "professional status" of the group that has them.

> Social workers consider themselves as full staff professionals. We are trained professionals; we are permanent members of the staff. But we get the same vacation, we are on the same kind of pay scale, as the maids and janitors.

Social workers want faculty status not merely for functions performed or to be performed—to teach medical students, but to *symbolize* their status as trained professionals. Nor is it only the privileges that are being sought, for these are only "marks" of prestige and "professional status." More basically, social workers want to be "treated" as *professional* people. And nonfaculty vacation privileges and pay scale mean—to them—that they are not accorded such treatment. "We are a profession; we are permanent staff; but in certain respects we are treated like these other personnel" (maids, janitors, secretaries).

Granted that academic rank is a symbol of prestige (professional status), it is still necessary to ascertain whose attitudes such rank (or its lack) symbolizes. Since the requests are directed toward the psychiatrists, the most obvious interpretation is that failure to grant them faculty status symbolizes psychiatrists' lack of professional respect for social workers.

However, it is possible that psychiatrists are merely the instrumentality for obtaining the symbol; the social workers may want the symbol to display to community members, relatives, and other members of the organization as a sign of achievement. The argument undoubtedly has merit. Also, social workers justify their claims to faculty status by pointing to the fact that several psychologists have academic rank. *Compared* to another "ancillary," they are not treated as equal professionals. Not to be rewarded with the privileges that psychologists have places social workers in a situation of *relative deprivation*—relative to another group the social workers are deprived.[8]

Still, the involvement of these features does not invalidate the interpretation that social workers place a high value on *psychiatrists'* "treating" them with professional respect, and that the granting of academic status would symbolize such respect. This is brought out most clearly when the power to grant faculty status for social workers is removed from the hands of the Department of Psychiatry.[9]

In this regard, a social worker, in commenting on nonfaculty vacation privileges, says:

We only get three weeks' vacation; the psychologists get a full month. This is contrary to national policy; we feel we have a right to be treated as equal professionals. Oh, it isn't the extra days that we don't get; but did you know that we get the same vacation that secretaries and janitors get? It's not that they [psychiatrists] can do anything about it, not now anyway; but if they really thought we were colleagues and competent professionals, they would, if they couldn't do something about it, say it ain't fair. They could let us know, at least, that they realize it isn't right.

8. On relative deprivation, see Robert K. Merton and Alice S. Kitt, "Contributions to the Theory of Reference Group Behavior," in Robert K. Merton and Paul F. Lazarsfeld (eds.), *Continuities in Social Research* (Glencoe: The Free Press, 1950), pp. 42-51.
9. Such power was always held in conjunction with the School of Medicine. The change that removed this ability from the hands of the Department of Psychiatry altogether will be discussed in the next chapter.

This statement indicates that several factors are involved in the faculty status request. There is an inconsistency between (perceived) national norms and organizational practice. There are the comparative reference groups of psychologists and non-professional personnel which social workers use to evaluate their own relative professional standing. But also, social workers want psychiatrists to indicate that they consider social workers professionally competent people who, therefore, have a *right* to professional privileges, even if they can no longer give them professional privileges. Faculty status is thus a prestige symbol, and although other groups are used as reference points to ascertain whether social workers have a right to faculty status, the desire to obtain it is very much oriented to the attitudes of psychiatrists. Psychiatrists function as an evaluative reference group, for it is from them that social workers want professional recognition. This becomes more explicit in the course of this chapter.

Failure to recognize faculty status as a symbol, with an attitudinal expressive structure being the more basic phenomenon, undoubtedly played a role in the psychiatrists' inability to understand the meaning of the request. Consequently, it did not "add up," and they were not sure how the social workers felt about it.

Regarding salary, social workers, like most other Americans, simply want more money. Yet, they do not want more money because they need it to survive—their salaries are adequate for that. Requests for higher salary are also an expression of a prestige problem, for money is an important prestige symbol in American society.[10] Involved in the social workers' request for more money is the "question of, is it [social work] valued and regarded. If they regard you highly, they will pay you more." Psychologists get more money than social workers; and although "this is not to disparage the psychologists," it is "a further status difference." Here again, what psychologists have is used as a reference point for making judgments regarding psychiatrists' respect for social workers, i.e., the value and "regard" they have for social workers.

Faculty status and income as symbols of "professional status," the meaning of professional status in terms of psychiatrists' respect for social workers, and the use of other groups as com-

10. See Talcott Parsons, "An Analytic Approach to the Theory of Social Stratification," in *Essays in Sociological Theory* (rev. ed.; Glencoe: The Free Press, 1954), esp. p. 430.

parative reference groups are all implicated in the following statement.

> There is this attitude here that a social worker doesn't have much of a professional contribution. Everywhere else the social worker is treated equal to the psychologists. They have faculty status but we don't. We get the same vacation as janitors and secretaries get. They pay them [psychologists] more than they pay us, too.

Thus, requests for more money, like the request for faculty status, is a "manifestation" of something else—regard and respect psychiatrists accord social workers. In addition, social workers not having "outside offices," [11] having to share offices when conditions are crowded, and no social worker making as much money as fifth-year resident fellows (although social workers "are full-time staff members and they aren't")—all are mentioned as reflecting "the lack of regard given to social workers as colleagues" by psychiatrists.

The major point to be underscored in this section on faculty status, salary, and other symbols of prestige is the fact that these are just that—symbols; and, to social workers, they reflect psychiatrists' evaluation of them. In the next section, attention is turned to a further specification of the perceived attitudes of psychiatrists.

PROFESSIONAL RESPECT: THE PERCEPTION OF PSYCHIATRISTS'
ATTITUDES AND THE PROBLEM OF PRESTIGE

The above section documents the social workers' prestige deprivation. In this section we will document in greater detail the social workers' concern with, and perception of, psychiatrists' attitudes toward them and show how the perception of such attitudes gives rise to prestige deprivation.

Statements in the previous section about not being "accepted" and "regarded" as "competent professionals" and as "colleagues" indicate that social workers want a particular kind of acceptance. They do not want acceptance as individual personalities. They want to be accepted and respected for their *work*. For example, one supervisor states that the social workers are "constantly fomenting" about "not being recognized, not being appreciated, their contribution not being respected. Many of their gripes are

11. Offices which have windows opening onto the outside.

against psychiatry not giving social work enough recognition." It is in reference to their work (their contribution) that social workers are primarily concerned about acceptance and respect.

This problem will be discussed under several categories. No claim is made that these categories are mutually exclusive; it will be apparent that they overlap at various points.

Work Is Not Considered Important

In Chapter 5 we noted the social workers' statements that residents do not consider their work important. Similarly, a social worker claims that senior psychiatrists have "doubts" as to the social workers' "worth" and that some have stated they do not need social workers. Another complains about not being listened to in ward rounds: The psychiatrist in charge may pick up "another patient's chart while I'm talking [and] the residents start looking at the nurse's report, and I'm left talking to a blank wall." One, who states that "more experienced psychiatrists" usually "see the need for social service and treating the family," also says, "There are some psychiatrists here who don't have much respect for social work." Still another maintains that despite the verbal adherence to the "holistic approach" in treating patients, psychiatrists actually emphasize intrapsychic conflict and rule out the importance of family relationships and, therefore, casework treatment with the family.

Seen in the Role of Welfare Worker

The previous description of the conflictive conceptions of the social worker role between the committee psychiatrists and the social workers reveals that the psychiatrists see the social work role as primarily one of welfare, rather than casework treatment with families.[12] For at least one social worker, this means that psychiatrists do not respect social workers as "knowledgeable professionals." This social worker complains about not being accepted as a "colleague"—she is not accepted as a collaborator. Instead, she is "seen as an ancillary"—that is, "someone who is [not] involved in the treatment process with the patient by working with his family." Although "I form a therapeutic relationship with the family," psychiatrists do not "see me as anyone with knowledge." Instead, "they see me in the role of someone

12. See p. 75 above.

who has knowledge about *concrete* and *specific* resources—such things as welfare, community agencies, clothing, and money."

She detects psychiatrists' failure to recognize her as competent in the area of treatment because when discussing problems of family guilt, anxiety, etc., "there have been times when I [am] asked, 'How do you know all this?' " In addition, her opinion in these areas is never solicited, whereas "there is no reluctance to ask me about financial assistance." In the same connection, another social worker, who considers herself a "professional with a body of knowledge," feels that "some psychiatrists fail to realize what a social worker is capable of contributing." They do not believe that social workers make "a professional contribution" or "to be useful for much but welfare and financial assistance."

To be seen as a welfare worker is, then, not to be seen as a knowledgeable professional. This suggests that the social workers' definition of their instrumental role (casework treatment with families) becomes importantly involved in the expressive orientation to be accorded professional respect and recognition by psychiatrists.[13]

Expressive Symbolism and the Educational Structure

As used in the present context, expressive symbolism refers to the ways in which the psychiatrists' evaluative attitudes of social workers are communicated to, and perceived by, the social workers.[14] Accordingly, the above analysis is a description of the phenomenon, expressive symbolism. For example, not to grant social workers academic status, or to define their role exclusively in the area of welfare, is interpreted by the social workers as a reflection (a symbol) of the psychiatrists' attitude toward them. Attention in this section is turned to certain symbolic aspects of the educational structure of the Department.

It will be recalled that all but one social worker states that the primary social work role is casework treatment with the family.[15] And the above indicates that social workers perceive psychia-

13. The place of the welfare role in the social workers' instrumental role definition, and its relationship to their expressive orientations, will be analyzed in detail in the next chapter.
14. Talcott Parsons defines the term "expressive symbolism" as "the communication of affect." See his discussion in *The Social System* (Glencoe: The Free Press, 1951), pp. 384-427.
15. See p. 64 above.

trists as failing to respect their ability and competence in this area. Such perception is due in part to this setting's being an academic department of a medical school, where educational objectives receive greater emphasis than is true of most social work settings. This has a twofold effect on social workers: (1) Social workers work primarily with psychiatric trainees (residents), rather than the senior staff. (2) Psychiatric trainees are given the opportunity to do in-take and work with families—"traditional social work functions." These, in turn, have major expressive consequences for social workers.

A consequence of the first is apparent in the following statement, made by a social worker in the context of discussing psychiatrists' tendency not to see the "importance" of social work.

> I'll give you an example of what I'm talking about. Social work is used in the team approach—we function on a team basis. But the physicians don't use social workers on private cases. We wondered why. We worked with the resident, but after he finishes he doesn't use us any more. We wondered why this should be if he wasn't going to use social workers when he became a psychiatrist anyway. We began to wonder why we weren't used on private cases. We only worked with the resident. We felt that they [psychiatrists] only wanted us to help with the training of the resident, not to contribute what we had been trained to do—to function as social workers.

Senior psychiatrists' failure to use social work services indicates—to social workers—that they do not think social workers make important contributions. Although working with residents does not preclude social workers from performing traditional social work tasks (i.e., casework) and operating as a member of the "team," it does symbolize and communicate psychiatrists' attitudes toward them: Psychiatrists want them to aid only in the training of residents, not to "function as social workers." In short, senior psychiatrists do not consider social workers to be very important insofar as psychiatric *treatment* is concerned. To use them in psychiatric education does not respect their professional competence.

The second aspect of the educational emphasis results in medical students' and residents' working with persons who are traditional social work clients. In light of the social workers' opinion of the competence of residents,[16] one would expect them to view this as an intrusion of unqualified personnel into their area of competence. For example, regarding in-take, "which is a traditional social work function, there is a lot of skill and competence involved [in] knowing how to handle people when they first come to the clinic." Consequently, "you need a skilled and competent person to do in-take."

> The family is often defensive when they first come to the clinic; you need a skilled person who can handle this. But social workers don't do this here, not as a rule. The emphasis is on teaching. There is a need for someone who is skilled in this area to work with the family and with the psychiatrists as a team.

Permitting the residents to do in-take and to work with the family

> can be rationalized and you can say that this is a training unit and the residents should have the responsibility. But working with the family and in-take are traditionally social work functions—these are national standards. You may be able to rationalize it in terms of training, but you need skilled and trained persons operating in these areas.

This complaint was not precipitated by residents' taking work away from social workers, for the respondent states that social workers do not have sufficient staff to perform all in-take and casework services. Consequently, its explanation must be sought elsewhere.

At the level of social structure, two closely related points are indicated. One is the conflict between the organization's norms and the national social work norms. Second is the allocation of role responsibilities; the social worker is dissatisfied with the allocation of "traditional social work functions" to residents. At the social-psychological level, a third point is revealed by another statement, made in reference to residents' performing social work functions.

> It's this attitude that they [psychiatrists] don't see anything special that a social worker contributes that they can't do without, or that a resident can't do, that is so irritating to us.

16. See p. 72 above.

Not Seen as a Group

Another feature involved in the social workers' feelings of not being accepted and respected as professionals is the fact that they are members of a professional *group*. Two social workers, both of whom feel that as *individuals* they have been accepted by the staff psychiatrist in charge of their particular units, express dissatisfaction about social workers not being accepted as a *group*.

> The primary dissatisfaction of the workers here comes in not being a unified group. We are not *seen* as a social work group. Oh, individually I get things worked out—I have no complaints as an individual. I couldn't be treated nicer. But there is no status here for a social worker. Not as an individual, as a social worker.

The other feels she is accepted by the psychiatrist in charge of her unit (inpatient service) as someone who is capable of performing a therapeutic role with the family, but it is a matter of his accepting "what *I* do." "What bothers me now is, as a group, we aren't accepted. As a group, we have a lack of status."

Both social workers associate their "status" (or lack thereof) with psychiatrists' tendency to "see" or "accept" social workers as a *group*. Clearly, the social workers' problem of prestige ("status") is a group phenomenon. Since it is also in reference to their work that social workers want and feel they have a right to "professional status" and "respect," the problem of not being seen as a group must be associated with the lack of respect and recognition accorded their work.

The phenomenon involved is illustrated by an event which took place between the social workers (including the one quoted immediately above) and a psychiatrist. The psychiatrist had just stated that the function of social workers had to do with welfare and economic assistance.

> Social Worker 1: —————, you know I've been doing casework with patients' relatives, don't you? I've been working with patients' relatives on your ward. How is that concerned with economic well-being?

> Psychiatrist: The reason I don't object is because of you. I don't know if I would let another social worker work with relatives or not. That shoots the whole formal scheme all to hell.

Social Worker 2: Seems to me you would expect something from *social work,* just as we expect something from psychiatry.

Social Worker 3: You let [social worker 1] work with relatives, but you don't know if you would let another social worker work with relatives. That's sort of an inconsistency, isn't it?

Psychiatrist: I told you before I live in a very small and biased world. I'm full of inconsistencies.

The psychiatrist evaluates the social worker as an individual, not as a member of the social work profession—or at least he says as much. As the social worker indicates in the interview, however, this kind of evaluation is not what she wants. She wants to be seen as a member of a group. This brings to attention the psychiatrists' tendency to ignore hierarchical and professional status differences and to try to deal with persons as "individuals." [17] Our concern, however, is with the consequences this may have for the social workers' desire to be accepted and seen as members of a group. There are two related problems involved.

First, the psychiatrist expresses respect for the *individual* social worker, but not because she is a social worker. Stated differently, he respects and accepts her because of her individual *performances,* not because of her *qualities* (membership in the profession of social work) which are possessed independently of the way she individually performs the role of social worker.[18] But she wants acceptance and respect on the basis of her status (qualities) as a social worker, not her individual performance. In one case she is accepted and respected as a professional; in the other she is accepted and respected as an individual.

Second, the social worker is dissatisfied because *other* social workers are not accepted. The psychiatrist does not respect a *category* of social workers, but a *particular* social worker. That is, he defines his relationship with her on *particularistic* grounds (i.e., "because of you"), rather than on *universalistic* grounds in which he would respect social workers generally because of

17. See Martin Loeb, "Role Definition in the Social World of a Psychiatric Hospital," in Milton Greenblatt, Daniel J. Levinson, and Richard H. Williams, *The Patient and the Mental Hospital* (Glencoe: The Free Press, 1957), pp. 14-19.

18. On the distinction between qualities and performances, see Talcott Parsons, Robert F. Bales, and Edward A. Shils, *Working Papers in the Theory of Action* (Glencoe: The Free Press, 1953), p. 66.

their professional competence.[19] Since it is only as a member of a group (social work) that the individual social worker can be a professional—that she can possess the quality of professional status—a psychiatrist's failure to respect social workers in general as competent professionals is also a failure to respect the individual social worker.

Not Recognized in the Role of Psychotherapist

Previous comments by social workers that they have a therapeutic relationship with the family and handle the "defensive" family suggest a tendency to define their casework relationship as a psychotherapeutic relationship. There are other indications that this is so. For example, social workers speak of handling relatives' "anxiety" and "guilt" that are created by the patient's hospitalization. Also, when a psychiatrist states, "Sometimes it's relatively worthless to see relatives," a social worker argues: "No, not for the relatives. They experience catharsis; get an understanding of what's going on." However, this same social worker maintains that although casework treatment with the relative is a "form of psychotherapy," psychiatrists accuse them of trying to be "junior psychiatrists," and this "influences the status of social work." Their ability to perform "a form of psychotherapy" is not recognized: When residents and medical students interview relatives, it is called therapy; when social workers do this, it is called casework. "In both cases it's the same thing, but in one case it's therapy and in the other it's not."

In their complaints about psychiatrists' depreciation of them, social workers often make reference to their "lack of status." This suggests that for their work not to be respected by psychiatrists gives social workers a feeling of low "status" or prestige. This is understandable, for, after all, others' recognition of the importance of one's work is what gives one a feeling of prestige in this organization. "Professional respect"—having one's work accepted and recognized as important and being accorded the privileges and symbols associated with "professional

19. For the distinction between universalism and particularism, see *ibid.* The desire for professional respect and recognition may well be the major factor in the tendency toward universalism in all professions, or as Wilensky and Lebeaux express it, the tendency "to foster the myth that all practitioners are equally able." Harold L. Wilensky and Charles N. Lebeaux, *Industrial Society and Social Welfare* (New York: Russell Sage Foundation, 1958), p. 304.

status"—is the essence of prestige in an organization composed of highly skilled occupational groups.

It is especially important to note that the social workers' prestige is dependent on the psychiatrists' evaluation of them. If psychiatrists fail to accord them the proper respect (or if the social workers feel that they do), they give social workers a feeling of low prestige, i.e., they create a "problem of low status." [20] Conversely, they have the power to confirm the social workers' image that they are professional persons. For example, regarding the change in the admissions procedure on the inpatient service,[21] an inpatient social worker states:

> One of the fine benefits that has accrued to it is that it represents from the staff that social workers are professionals and have something professional to contribute to the patients' treatment when the patients first come here. It symbolizes psychiatry's acceptance of us.

The above discussion outlines various ways in which social workers express concern and dissatisfaction with the way they are evaluated by psychiatrists, independent of their desire for prestige *privileges*. The psychiatrists' evaluation of them is important in and of itself. This is not to say that all social workers express such concern in the same way; it is to say, however, that, with two exceptions to be noted in the next chapter, all social workers express dissatisfaction with the psychiatrists' attitude toward them.

It was stated that this concern revolves around the way their *work* is evaluated. In addition, there are indications that social workers want to be given proper consideration and "regard" in areas not directly related to their work. In this connection, they were in opposition to the writer's presence as an observer in the committee meetings. Their opposition did not stem from the fact that they were to be observed, however.

> When decisions are made about us, we want them to ask us our judgments and opinions. This was one of the things involved in the committee meetings, and your coming in. It was the way they handled it. They didn't let us know you were coming in—they just told us. Just like that.

20. An explanation of why social workers should be so dependent on psychiatrists for prestige is offered in the next chapter.
21. See pp. 79-82 above.

Finally, one social worker thinks that proper respect is not given to social workers' opinion by psychiatrists in the hiring of psychiatrists.

> After he [prospective staff member] has come for his interview and we have met and talked with him, they can ask us our opinion about him. They can ask us what we think about him, how he might work in a team setting. But, of course, we shouldn't be asked if we think he should be hired. Certainly, not that. But they can ask us our opinion of him.

It is important to be recognized and respected, even if it has no effect on the psychiatrists' decision.

ROLE OF PSYCHIATRIC SOCIAL WORK SUPERVISOR

A description of the supervisor's role will underscore further the social workers' need for the psychiatrists' positive evaluation, as well as their deprivation in this regard. Actually this role can be understood only in terms of its expressive functions for social workers. Consideration of the social workers' need for "better channels to the administration to work on our problems" will introduce us to these functions.

Upon being told of this need during the committee meetings, the psychiatrists stated they did not know what social workers meant by "administrative channels." They maintained that social workers were responsible to the supervisor and that "there can't be any other way." They then asked if better channels were needed in order to work out problems on the three service units —child, outpatient, and inpatient. The social workers replied that the problem was a more general one. It was a matter of having better administrative channels to solve "things that are problems for the social workers as a group." One stated:

> I have been able to work out with Dr. _____ problems on the inpatient service, but he can't do anything about certain problems that concern the social service as a whole. We don't have an opportunity to work out some of the problems as a group. The channel from _____ [supervisor] to _____ [Department head] gets foggy.

At this time, social workers proposed the establishment of an administrative committee—a "regular standing committee" of psychiatrists,[22] for which the psychiatrists saw no need. Reasons social workers gave, other than the fact that they worked closely with the psychiatrist in the team,[23] are as follows.

[We need] someone we can go to with our problems. We need a committee close to us, one that understands us and our point of view.

We need someone more than Mr. _____ [supervisor].

It's done in other places. It's considered good administration. There is a need for a committee that we can always go to.

It's considered good administration to have a social service standing committee.

Two points should be emphasized. First, psychiatrists do not understand what social workers mean by "administrative channels" nor their need for the proposed committee, and raise questions regarding its need in reference to work—instrumental—problems (i.e., in reference to the individual service units). They fail to see the possibility of a group function. Second, although the social workers are not explicit as to what their "problems as a group" are, they see them in connection with the social work supervisor: "Someone more than" the supervisor is needed to work on their "group problems." Consequently, analysis of the supervisor's functions should throw light on these problems. It should also indicate what is meant by "inadequate and unclear administrative channels," and why there is the need for a "regular standing committee" of psychiatrists.

The committee psychiatrists informed the writer that the social workers had individually expressed to them that the supervisor was "generally incompetent" and "not strong enough." One psychiatrist felt that the latter complaint was "overemphasized by the females" and implied that the problem was due to a conflict between sexes—the female social workers needed to "castrate" the supervisor.[24] It is our interpretation that social workers were dissatisfied with the supervisor for performing certain expressive

22. See p. 77 above.
23. See p. 77 above.
24. In this same connection, a social worker states that rather than psychiatrists' viewing social workers as a group with professional problems to work out, "they say our problems are due to sex differences—we're women."

functions inadequately. The expressive function involved in not being "strong enough" will be described and analyzed first.

THE SUPERVISOR AS THE "LINK" TO THE ADMINISTRATION

Examination of the supervisor's conception of his role and the social workers' conception indicates consensus regarding his role.

The Supervisor's Definition

Instrumental functions.—Like other social workers, the supervisor performs casework services and does some teaching of medical students (although his formal teaching responsibilities are somewhat greater). He states that he acts as casework supervisor for other social workers; they come to him for his opinion on their handling of cases. He is also involved in the hiring of social workers. Finally, the supervisor performs a liaison role with other social work agencies and schools of social work, all communications with these agencies going through him. An aspect of this function is to arrange training opportunities for social work students.

Expressive functions.—From the supervisor's standpoint, there are two primary expressive functions. One is "to promote the professional development" of social workers—e.g., arrange meetings and seminars for the social workers. The other is to be the "link to the administration" [for] anything of interest to social workers.

> I take care of problems of salary, faculty status and take these up with _____ [Department head]. This is the social workers' link with the administration [psychiatrists]. Anything of interest to social work I take care of. That's my job—to keep them happy.

Similarly, the supervisor works through the head of the Department to get expense money for social workers to attend professional conferences and meetings.

Social Workers' Definition[25]

Instrumental functions.—Aside from the liaison role and ar-

---

25. The following is based on responses volunteered by social workers or in reply to the query of what they considered the supervisor's functions to be. In the event that such information was volunteered, the question was usually not asked.

ranging training opportunities for social work students, no social worker indicates any instrumental need for this position. Each states that work problems are solved either by working with the head psychiatrist or head social worker of his unit.[26]

Expressive functions.—Social workers agree that the supervisor should arrange for seminars and work with the administration (psychiatrists) on the problems of vacation, salary, and faculty status.

It appears that casework supervision—which none of the social workers mention—is the only point of disagreement between the supervisor and social workers. No one mentions this as a source of dissatisfaction, however. Thus, the social workers' dissatisfaction with the supervisor is not created by a lack of consensus regarding the latter's role. Rather, it is the supervisor's moving too slowly on the fronts of salary increases, academic status, sick leave, and vacation privileges. Various complaints are of this nature, and give credence to the psychiatrists' statement that the group felt the supervisor was "not strong enough." This is expressed in several ways: he was not "moving fast enough with things," he "couldn't get anything done," he "was not backing our requests," "we felt that he wasn't working in our behalf," or he "wasn't supporting us." Consequently:

> One of the major problems of the social workers was we found it unsatisfactory to work through Mr. _____. We felt that he wasn't working in our behalf [on salary, vacation, and sick leave]. We would take problems to him but things weren't moving as fast as they should have.

The supervisor's views are consistent with the social workers'. He claims social workers have accused him of not "supporting them," not having their "interest at heart," and not being "concerned with the interests of the social workers." For example:

> There was the problem of salary. This is always hard. In the eyes of the social workers I wasn't moving fast enough. And there was faculty status—they thought they should have faculty status. I moved on these fronts as fast as I thought the climate of opinion would admit.

The "climate of opinion" is his perception of psychiatrists'

26. In addition to a supervisor for the over-all psychiatric social work group, there is a psychiatric social work supervisor on the inpatient and child psychiatric services.

opinion of social work. He states that psychiatrists question "the value of the contributions a social worker makes," and have "an equivocal attitude as to the social workers' worth." Although some realize the social workers' value, "others seem to have the attitude that they are probably useful for something—but are they worth all the trouble?" He also felt he "wasn't being given the proper support" by some of the higher ranking psychiatrists. For example, one of the top psychiatrists had commented to other psychiatrists in the supervisor's presence "that psychiatry didn't need social work. . . . He quoted this to a bunch of psychoanalysts in front of me." There were also occasions when a top psychiatrist said "that social work is all mixed up. Like social workers didn't know what they were doing, where they were going, what their role was—just mixed up. He often expressed [to me] that psychiatry didn't need social work." Consequently, he was reluctant to appear to be "asking for too much."

> I didn't want _____ [Department head] to think I was asking for too much. I knew how he felt about social work. The social workers would be down here putting pressure on me, wanting something from the administration; I would often be hesitant about taking it to _____ [Department head] because of this attitude. The social workers would want something done right away. I wanted to go slow.

Indeed, the supervisor claims he could have gotten the things social workers wanted—salary, faculty status, vacation, sick leave—only by going slowly. These are also the matters about which social workers accused him of not moving fast enough. This is why they were dissatisfied with him.

It has been shown that the social workers were concerned about the psychiatrists' attitude toward them. Thus, at a more basic level, it would seem that the supervisor's "weakness" was his inability to change the psychiatrists' appraisal and evaluation of the social workers. Although his perception of the psychiatrists' attitudes was not unlike the other social workers—he, too, expressed dissatisfaction with the lack of respect accorded social workers—evidence indicates that he was less willing to combat this depreciative attitude. For example, during one committee meeting when the problems of salary, academic status, and a lack of acceptance as "colleagues" were voiced, he stated that he had tried to get social workers to "accept their situation"; he argued that they "should be able to derive satisfaction from working with families and making a contribution." In an interview he takes an even stronger position.

Social work in a psychiatric setting is an ancillary profession. When you are ancillary, by definition, you aren't as important as the major profession—and here the major profession is psychiatry. Also, here there is a greater emphasis placed on research and teaching than on service, and it is service for which social workers are trained. Service is important, but teaching and research are more important. Social work is more service oriented and, therefore, not as important as some of the others.

And to accept an "ancillary" role has the following consequences for the expressive orientations of social workers.

Whenever the social workers have felt that they weren't getting enough status, prestige, attention, and all that, I had to help them to realize they were doing a good job. That's all we can be concerned about here. The medical student and resident are the darlings. We have to be ancillary—that's the way it should be. This is a medical setting which emphasizes the education of the residents and medical students. They are the ones who get the attention—that's the way it should be; it has to be that way.

It is actually difficult to assess the supervisor's position on this issue. On several occasions he expressed dissatisfaction with the psychiatrists' opinion of social workers. In the above statements he argues that the social workers' contribution is not as important as the contribution of others; they should be satisfied merely doing their work, and thus forgo "status, prestige, attention, and all that." It is not known if he takes this position because he is less desirous of a favorable evaluation from psychiatrists, or because he wants the social workers to accept their situation and thereby reduce pressure on him. On still other occasions, he takes a position between the social workers and psychiatrists, becoming the proverbial "man in the middle."

The social workers make a valuable contribution, but maybe not as much as they like. The psychiatrists are at the other end. I have the problem of reconciling the two. It's difficult. Neither party is happy.

In any case, the supervisor—"the link to the administration"— did not produce. He wanted to "go slow" on privileges; the social workers thought he was not "moving fast enough." He was willing to forgo prestige and accept an "ancillary" position. But prestige was a value other social workers were not willing to forgo.

With the above analysis in mind, the problem of "administrative channels" can be seen in clearer perspective. The supervisor was the "link to the administration" for faculty status, salary, etc. Consequently, it would seem that the administrative committee, which is necessary because social workers "need someone more than" the supervisor, was proposed in order to facilitate the social workers' quest for academic status, salary increases, and possibly other privileges. It was, in other words, a strategy designed to supplement (or replace) the supervisor and thereby facilitate the social workers' expressive orientations. One social worker does, in fact, explicitly mention it in these terms, since "problems of faculty status and promotions could be ironed out by the committee."

There is evidence that the committee is more directly associated with the perception of the psychiatrists' attitudes. A social worker claims that the committee would have been useful to discuss what the social workers' contribution could be in the training program of the Department; this suggests a need for the committee to perform an instrumental function. However,

> it's good for morale to have a feeling of group unity with the Department, and for them to show a concern with our contribution. Not a day-by-day work thing, but a contribution in terms of mutual understanding between the professions. Before [the proposed committee] our channel was Mr. _____ [supervisor]. We need to have a broader base.

For at least one social worker, then, the committee is definitely associated with psychiatrists' evaluation of social work. This suggests that the committee's function of "improving communication" refers to the communication of a certain attitude from psychiatrists to social workers: the committee would have symbolized psychiatrists' "concern" with the social workers' contribution. It also suggests that what social workers mean by their statements that "administrative channels" are "unclear," "inadequate," and "foggy" is that psychiatrists are not communicating the attitudes to them that they want and feel they have a right to expect. Whether or not this inference is valid, the analysis of the expressed problem of "inadequate and unclear administrative channels" does reveal the supervisor's involvement in the problem. Also, the association of this problem with the problems of salary, faculty status, and professional acceptance and respect is clearly revealed when the expressive role of the supervisor is considered.

As noted above, there was another complaint about the supervisor, one having to do with his "incompetence." This must be viewed in terms of the supervisor's symbolic role as leader of the social work group.

THE SYMBOLIC ROLE OF THE SUPERVISOR

To this point the supervisor's role has been interpreted as an instrumentality for gratifying social workers' expressive orientations. That role was a symbolic one only in that the things for which he was responsible (e.g., obtaining faculty status for social workers) symbolized psychiatrists' respect for, and acceptance of, social workers as colleagues and professionals. Although he did not perform this role to the satisfaction of other social workers, he was aware of the role and accepted it.

In addition, social workers attributed another role to him. The psychiatrists state that social workers complain about the supervisor's being "generally incompetent." [27] A consideration of the expressive features of leadership roles suggests the nature of this complaint.

In a discussion of "the expressive aspects of leadership roles," Talcott Parsons states that "the common value sentiments which constitute the collectivity are projected upon the leader as a symbolic embodiment of these values." [28] For the collectivity of social workers, a central "value sentiment" is the feeling of professional competence. They feel they are skilled and competent professionals, and they want psychiatrists to treat them accordingly. It is therefore understandable that they would want the supervisor to uphold this image in his relations with psychiatrists. There is evidence that social workers thought he did not. For example, one social worker states that he was "respected" by neither the social workers nor the psychiatrists. Another draws the conclusion from this that the psychiatrists *wanted* the supervisor. "He

27. See p. 175 above. The supervisor felt that the psychiatrists, as well as the social workers, "lend credence to the view that I [am not] as competent and all-knowing as I should be."
28. Talcott Parsons, *The Social System*, p. 400.

had been here for five years and had been incompetent all this time, yet they kept him." The psychiatrists kept what they considered an "incompetent" social work leader; therefore, they wanted an "incompetent" social work leader. Consequently, to keep him reflected their opinion of the social workers.

> All along there has been a lot of resentment by us toward the administration [psychiatrists] because of _____ [supervisor]. We felt that this symbolized their attitude toward the social workers. We felt, again for dual reasons, because _____ was the way he is [incompetent] and because the administration [psychiatrists] wanted it that way, that they wanted a subsidiary group.[29] They did not want a collaborative function from us.

Thus, not to respect their leader as competent is not to respect the social work *group*. To retain his services when they consider him incompetent reflects the psychiatrists' opinion of the social workers themselves. Consequently, the social workers were dissatisfied with the supervisor. Two stated that social workers "resented" the psychiatrists' retaining his services. It was not just the fact that social workers felt the supervisor was incompetent; psychiatrists also thought so. "The psychiatrists felt that he was incompetent too. That was the worst part." This was worse because "If they thought he was incompetent, what did they think about the rest of the social workers."

The supervisor's failure to perform his expressive functions for the social workers led at least two of them to feel that he "identified too strongly with the psychiatrists"; "we felt that he identified with psychiatry, that he had a need to please the psychiatrists, not the social workers." They saw the supervisor adopting the psychiatrists' attitude toward them: "He was identifying with the psychiatrists—taking their point of view toward us."[30]

These data question the psychiatrist's interpretation that the social workers' dissatisfaction with the supervisor derives from their need to castrate him. In fact, evidence indicates that dis-

29. The respondent indicates that by "subsidiary group" she means one that will do whatever the doctor asks them to do—e.g., see the patient's "wife in order to keep her from leaving the husband," rather than a group with a "body of knowledge, and competent to use it" in a therapeutic capacity with the patient's family.
30. As was noted above, because of the supervisor's inconsistency, it is not possible to determine if he were really "identifying with the psychiatrists."

satisfaction is not even related to sex. Shortly after the committee meetings, the supervisor's position was eliminated in an administrative change affecting the social workers. He terminated employment, and the functions of the social work supervisor were taken over by a medical social worker who became social work supervisor for all hospital social workers. Regarding the old supervisor, a social worker states that they were dissatisfied with him because they had been unable to get across to psychiatrists the importance of the social workers' contribution: "We weren't able to clarify our own function to various people. No one really seemed to understand just what social work did." Thus, the supervisor was held accountable, at least in part, for the fact that psychiatrists did not know what the social workers "can or should contribute." Another social worker, who feels that psychiatrists see social workers as a "subsidiary" group, states of the new supervisor: "She has the same problems that _____ had. She is really no different from him." The new supervisor is not liked because she is willing to accept social work in a "subsidiary role"—"she thinks that social workers should do anything and everything that a doctor asks them to do," rather than perform a collaborative and treatment role. In essence, she is unwilling to do anything about the "problems we've always had," namely, the problem of psychiatric social work's being defined "as a subservient role, rather than one of professional competence, one that has professional knowledge, and is capable of acting on that knowledge."

It is worth noting that, in this same interview, the above social worker says she no longer considers herself "as put upon in a subservient role." As an individual, she thinks her psychiatric supervisor has accepted her as someone who performs a therapeutic role with the family. The complaints against the supervisor are, therefore, addressed to the supervisor's failure to perform a function for the social work group.

These findings concerning the supervisor, and other data in this chapter, point to one major conclusion: it is not sufficient for social workers to see themselves as possessing the quality of "professional status"; it is necessary for psychiatrists to recognize their "professional status." The social worker's professional self-image requires confirmation from psychiatrists.

REACTIONS TO EXPRESSIVE DEPRIVATION

In light of the sociologist's long recognition that persons perceive themselves only in terms of the attitudes and opinions of others,[31] the dependence of social workers' self-images on others' attitudes is understandable.[32] The problem now is to analyze the social workers' reaction to expressive deprivation which stems from the psychiatrists' failure to confirm their self-picture.

Two strategies which have already been discussed—attempts to evoke a norm and create an administrative committee of psychiatrists—may be seen in terms of their expressive properties. The administrative committee has been commented upon in the section on the supervisor's role. The norm social workers attempted to evoke would have specified that social workers would perform casework treatment with families, thus creating a normative definition of the social work role consistent with the social workers' own definition. When we recall that social workers also wanted psychiatrists to recognize them as competent in the area of family treatment, it follows that if psychiatrists had specified the above definition, it would have reflected their respect for and acceptance of the social workers' professional competence. This conclusion receives some confirmation from an interview with one of the social workers.

The respondent in question states that she had tried to get an explicit statement regarding the social workers' duties. She claims that she has been unable to do so because social workers are not highly valued by psychiatrists.

> The social worker doesn't have any status so she can't get any changes made. It is in the administrative structure that the trouble really lies. If we are going to get any changes made in social work services, it will have to come through there. But they will have to see the need for social service. When they think we have a value, then it will come.

The change to which the subject refers is the establishment of a clear statement from psychiatrists regarding the social worker's functions, which this respondent defines as casework treatment

31. Charles H. Cooley, *Human Nature and the Social Order* (New York: Charles Scribner's Sons, 1922); and George H. Mead, *Mind, Self, and Society*, ed., Charles N. Morris (Chicago: University of Chicago Press, 1934).
32. But why psychiatrists are so important in this respect is a question postponed until the next chapter.

and in-take—"traditional social work functions." Psychiatrists will introduce the change when they place a value on social work. And, conversely, if the change should come—if psychiatrists should specify that they expect social workers to work in the above areas—it would symbolize an attitude of respect for the importance, skill, and competence of social workers.[33] Thus, if their attempt to evoke the norm had been successful, it would have become an expressive symbol reflecting psychiatrists' recognition of the social workers' value. Seen in this light, the attempt may be viewed as a strategy which would have established an "appreciative standard," [34] one which would be consistent with the social workers' professional self-images.

The two examples—the attempt to evoke a norm and the proposed administrative committee—illustrate the point that instrumental and expressive orientations are only analytically, not concretely, independent. The norm would have had both instrumental and expressive consequences: it would have facilitated the acquisition of referrals as well as having symbolized psychiatrists' positive evaluation of social work. Accordingly, it would have been compounded with instrumental value as well as expressive value.

In light of the description of the recreation service and clinical psychology, we would expect expressive deprivation to pose problems of a different nature than those encountered on an instrumental level, differences that the above two strategies do not reveal. Expressive deprivation, we remember, is a problem of others' attitudes. And the recreator's and psychologists' experiences indicate the difficulty of coercing the expression of desired attitudes. Comments from the two social work supervisors throw additional light on this problem.

We recall the supervisor's remarks about going slowly. His reasoning was as follows: "I felt we would have to show our competence first. I felt it would be better this way rather than to strive for these things [e.g., salary increases, academic rank] all at once and too fast." It is to be noted that the respondent

33. As a matter of fact, the inclusion of the inpatient social workers in the in-take process did have this effect for at least one social worker. See p. 173 above.
34. On appreciative standards, see Talcott Parsons and Edward A. Shils, *Toward A General Theory of Action* (Cambridge: Harvard University Press, 1951), esp. p. 60; on the relationship between expressive orientations and appreciative standards, see pp. 73 and 75.

correlates the social workers' show of competence with their right to certain prestige privileges, again emphasizing the point that prestige in this organization refers to others viewing you as professionally competent. Also, the comment once more reveals the social workers' need to be regarded by psychiatrists as competent (e.g., they "have to show [their] competence" to psychiatrists). The statement that they will have to show their competence first indicates that prestige is a phenomenon that must be achieved rather than ascribed: To be recognized as competent you must *first* demonstrate your competence.

For example, one supervisor states: "No one can give [ascribe] you status. You earn [achieve] status. If you make a contribution, it will be recognized and appreciated." Also, it is not a problem of social workers' "being granted status" because "status is earned, not given. If you show your competence, you will have status." Implied is the notion that you cannot *make* another accord you prestige ("status"). Therefore, "you don't fight for status, you earn it. When you demonstrate your competence, it will be recognized." In other words, rather than trying to "make" another adopt a positive attitude toward you, you prove your worth to him. In this connection, note the psychiatrist's remarks that social workers will have to "prove [they] are worthy," "prove [they] can make a contribution"; then they will be accepted.[35]

Excluding the two reactions mentioned above, reactions to the problem of not being accorded the proper acceptance and respect will be classified under four different categories. No claim is made that these are exhaustive of such reactions; they are only four which are suggested on the basis of the data at hand. In their order of presentation, these reaction types are personalized feelings and emotional reactions, emotional attachment to symbols, vicious circle, and leaving the organization.

Personalized Feelings and Emotional Reactions

The reaction referred to here is a feeling state which results from the social workers' perception of the psychiatrists' depreciative attitudes.

A social worker, upon hearing a psychiatrist say that he does not use social workers, states: "Yes, we knock on his door, he runs us away, and we get our feelings hurt. Then he has to come

35. See p. 76 above.

and pat us on the shoulder and make us feel good." Another "resents" being seen in an "ancillary role," that is, "not considered to be involved in the treatment process, not performing a treatment function." Along with such "resentment," this member feels that social workers are not "accepted" as professional persons. In commenting on psychiatrists' tendency not to consider social workers' "opinions and judgments" when departmental changes are made, especially those which affect the social workers, one social worker cites, for example, an administrative change which integrated psychiatric social workers with medical social workers. This respondent was disturbed by the fact that the psychiatric social workers' opinions were not considered in the change, and that no psychiatrist "asked any social worker how it's been going" during the year the change had been in effect. This policy of not asking the social workers for their opinions and judgments "doesn't feel good."

> It makes us feel like a step-child, that we are here but haven't been accepted for what we really are. It feels like we are cut off from the administration; no group unity or feeling of belonging to the Department. It makes use feel that they don't consider us as making a very important contribution.

Implied in the concept of implementing strategy is the notion that this strategy tends to be the most immediate reaction to instrumental deprivation. Emotional reactions, on the other hand, would seem to be the most immediate reactions to expressive deprivation and a lack of prestige. This is not to say that social workers themselves identify their lack of prestige as the source of these reactions, however. For example, one social worker, who feels that medical personnel do not see social work "as making a very important contribution," states:

> On occasion I'm inclined to get paranoid feelings about this and on the defensive. I get my feelings hurt because I'm not included in certain areas. But that's me personally, not social work. It's my personality, not status or social work; it has nothing to do with social work.

This suggests that because a lack of prestige (in the form of not being seen as one who makes "a very important contribution") produces an emotional reaction, the reaction is interpreted as due to something "inside" the individual, i.e., as due to "personality," and not "status" or social work.

Emotional Attachment to Symbols

Since the social workers' basic expressive problem is one of not receiving a respectful evaluation from psychiatrists, a direct attack on the problem would be to "correct" the (perceived) psychiatrists' opinion of social work. The above remarks indicate, however, that social workers do not always associate their problem of "status" with the way they are "respected," "accepted," and "seen" by psychiatrists. Still, there are instances where this is more or less clearly perceived, as is indicated by the social worker who realizes that the requests for salary increases and academic status are "manifestations of something else." Nevertheless, at least part of their feeling stemming from prestige deprivation crystallizes around objects (salary, academic status, supervisor) that symbolize the (perceived) attitudes of psychiatrists. Seen from this perspective, the social workers' request for additional salary and academic status may be viewed as reactions to expressive deprivation, but reactions which focus on symbols rather than the source of their deprivation—the psychiatrists' attitudes.

There is some evidence that the entire problem may crystallize around symbols. Parsons speaks of "scapegoat" symbolism, where individuals—particularly those carrying responsibility—become "targets" onto which the group's problems are projected.[36] This process is involved in the social workers' dissatisfaction with the supervisor. For example, one social worker claims that the supervisor is completely to blame for the psychiatrists' failure to respect social workers as competent professionals. In discussing this lack of acceptance and respect, the respondent states:

> This wouldn't happen if we had a strong leader secure in his role of social work. I don't know if this is clear, but if we had a strong leader, someone who could really identify with social work and be secure in this role and not be weak, we wouldn't have these problems.

The social workers were dissatisfied with their supervisor because of the latter's inability to implement the social workers'

36. Parsons, *The Social System*, p. 404.

expressive goals. These goals involved the privileges of academic rank and salary increases, but the basic problem was to get professional respect and acceptance from psychiatrists. Thus, a "strong" leader who "identified with social work" could get professional acceptance for social workers. While it is true that the social workers were dissatisfied with their supervisor, it stemmed in great part from, and was a reaction to, the way they were evaluated by psychiatrists. The supervisor was considered "weak," but the "weakness" lay in his inability to influence (i.e., change) the psychiatrists' opinion of social work. The social workers attribute the problem to "weak" leadership, not to psychiatrists' failure to accord them respect.

Vicious Circle

Regarding the social workers' complaints about a "lack of status" and their requests for academic status and increases in salary, the supervisor states, "Social workers, by and large, have been preoccupied with getting more money, more recognition, and more status." Psychiatrists, however, doubt the social workers' value, and "question whether or not the social workers deserve it [more money]. This equivocal attitude on the part of the administration [psychiatrists] as to the social workers' worth has been sensed by the social workers. This brings a reaction, an over-reaction, on the part of the social workers to reassert their worth by demanding higher salaries. This is met by a more equivocal attitude by the administration."

If the supervisor's description is an accurate one, it suggests that when the expressive needs of one group are not reciprocated by another group, relations between the two may become involved in a "vicious circle." One group, not receiving the desired reciprocating response from the other, may increase its demands only to have the other fail to reciprocate and have further doubts as to the former's worth. Consequently, the deprived group may make irrational demands that "do not add up." [37]

Note that requests for salary and academic status are not only reactions to the psychiatrists' treatment of them; they are also aimed at getting psychiatrists to recognize them as persons who possess "professional status." Such reactions may not attain their

37. One of the committee psychiatrists did, in fact, tell the writer that many of the social workers' requests during the committee were not "completely rational.

objective, however. In fact, they may have the reverse effect. A comment from the supervisor is suggestive.

> There are twenty-two psychiatrists. Some realize the value of social work. Others seem to have the attitude that they are probably useful for something but are they worth all the trouble. They give something of the feeling of, are the social workers worth all the trouble? Social workers then sense this. They take the attitude of, Goddamit, we are going to make you acknowledge our worth, by God. It's like a child who doesn't get love and attention from his parents. He acts out. This may further annoy and alienate the parent. This brings out a further acting out. He comes to be rejected. And so on.

It is a mistake, of course, to say that social workers want psychiatrists to "love" them. They do want professional respect and recognition, however. The supervisor's remarks indicate that the attempts to obtain respect and recognition through requests for prestige privileges were not successful. In fact, he implies that they had the reverse effect, i.e., social workers were "rejected" like the child. Similarly, another social worker, who in commenting on social workers' "resenting" the psychiatrists' "attitude that our work is not very important," says:

> But when we have been aggressive, act out, and make demands, the reaction is, why do you want to be a bunch of trouble makers? Why do you want to grumble so much? Treating us like bad girls who speak up to papa, not as professional people with problems to work out.

This "acting out" (requesting higher salaries and academic rank) may result in a self-fulfilling prophecy.[38] The social workers' definition of the situation is one in which the psychiatrists do not accord them professional respect. The consequences of their reaction to this definition—demanding professional privileges—is a perpetuation, or even an exaggeration, of the definition (e.g., being treated like "bad girls" rather than as "professional people"). Also, one social worker states that because of their requests for academic status, more money, and additional privileges, social workers have come to be defined as persons primarily interested in furthering their prestige: "All they say we want is status, privileges, and money."

38. Robert K. Merton, "The Self-Fulfilling Prophecy," *Social Theory and Social Structure* (rev. ed.; Glencoe: The Free Press, 1957), pp. 421-36.

Leaving the Organization

The above deals with reactions to prestige deprivation insofar as social workers remain members of the Department. During the course of the study, four social workers, all of whom had expressed dissatisfaction with the way social workers were evaluated by psychiatrists, terminated employment. To what extent such dissatisfaction entered into all four's leaving is not known, although one claimed that faculty status, salary, and the psychiatrists' depreciation of social workers were important factors in her decision to leave.

SUMMARY AND CONCLUSIONS

Findings of this chapter reveal the existence of a drive for greater prestige among social workers and their dependence on psychiatrists for prestige confirmation (and disconfirmation). The desire for prestige, in turn, is associated with the social workers' conception of their professional status. The drive for higher prestige is inseparable from the desire to obtain professional status. It is in connection with the drive for greater prestige —more specifically, the desire for a higher appraisal and evaluation from psychiatrists—that salary and academic rank are viewed as symbols of prestige and of professional status.

The prestige structure of this setting, along with the drive for greater prestige, creates problems for the social workers. This organization, like all complex organizations, contains gradations of prestige—e.g., from nonprofessional personnel up to psychologists and psychiatrists. Social workers consider themselves the equal of psychologists and as colleagues to psychiatrists. Dissatisfaction results because social workers perceive psychiatrists as treating them as employees rather than as professional staff. The existence of a prestige hierarchy in which personnel are accorded differential treatment, i.e., in which some are accorded the symbols and recognition of professional status and others are not, provides the social workers with comparative reference points to make evaluations of themselves. Hence, the problem of prestige is greatly one of relative deprivation. Such problems become especially acute in a mental hospital because of the existence of several highly skilled professional groups who are not, and cannot be, accorded equal prestige.

Other aspects of the organization which contribute to the social workers' prestige deprivation are the educational emphasis of the Department, role definition of welfare worker rather than as therapist, not being seen and accepted as a group, and social work leadership (and "administrative channels"). In all of these features, however, the underlying theme is the lack of professional respect, acceptance, and recognition accorded their work by psychiatrists.

Data in this chapter also reveal how aspects of an organization may become compounded with both expressive and instrumental properties. This is especially true in the case of the social worker who sees the change in the inpatient admission procedure as a reflection of psychiatrists' professional acceptance of social workers. Also, it was suggested that if the strategies of evoking a norm and formation of an administrative committee had been successful, they would have facilitated the social workers' expressive orientations, as well as their performance of the instrumental casework role.

Nevertheless, data are consistent with findings on the expressive orientations of the recreator and psychologists in that they suggest that the problem of expressive deprivation is sufficiently different from problems involved in instrumental role performance to warrant separate consideration. The difference derives from the fact that the problem of eliciting desired instrumental responses from others is one of obtaining overt acts, while the problem of eliciting a desired expressive response is one of receiving attitudinal responses (respect, acceptance, appreciation, recognition). A failure to obtain these responses is seen to result in emotional reactions ("hurt feelings," feelings of being "cut off," no feeling of acceptance or belonging) which, in turn, become attached to various symbols within the organization. In this process, it was further suggested that the deprived social workers may come to make irrational demands and to become implicated in a vicious circle with the psychiatrists, possibly leading to a self-fulfilling prophecy.

11 SOCIAL WORK: RELATIONSHIP BETWEEN INSTRUMENTAL ROLE DEFINITION AND EXPRESSIVE DEPRIVATION

In the present chapter we turn to differences among the social workers. In Chapter 5 we saw the social workers' emphasis on the casework treatment dimension of their role. Here, we consider the problem of instrumental role definition in greater detail, and will give consideration to two social workers who deviate from other social workers in this regard. We will also continue the analysis of expressive deprivation as described in the previous chapter, where we found that the social workers' expressive deprivation was essentially a problem of prestige, that is, their perception of psychiatrists' depreciation of them. Consideration will now be given to social workers who indicate no concern with the psychiatrists' evaluation of them. A comparison of these social workers with the others will suggest that instrumental orientation (role definition) and expressive orientation (prestige deprivation) are related.

193

ROLE DEFINITION

According to a study by Harold L. Wilensky and Charles N. Lebeaux, casework is the dominant specialty in social work and social workers could have no professional identity without it. Although there are other social work specialties (e.g., group work), casework is *the* "area of competence" in social work.[1]

In light of this, we would conclude that social workers who define their role as primarily one of casework treatment are in agreement with the national norm of their profession. There is one social worker who sees the role of social worker differently, however. She defines her role in terms of departmental aims rather than the profession of social work. This worker will be referred to as the "local," in contrast to the other social workers who will be called the "cosmopolitans."[2] The distinction means that cosmopolitans define their role primarily in terms of professional social work norms rather than the goals of the Department, whereas the local defines her role primarily in reference to the goals of the Department.

THE LOCAL

First of all, the local accepts the fact that the Department is not a social work organization: "The over-all function is not a social work function; I am concerned with how to improve the over-all service of the unit, not just to improve social work." In regard to what the over-all function is, she states:

> I think personally—some of the other social workers disagree with me, but I let the unit itself decide. Ultimately, good patient care and teaching coincide, but some place along the line one must be given the ultimate priority. This is a teaching setting for psychiatric trainees and so teaching is usually given the primary consideration. Some [social workers] think that it should not be this way, but the major purpose of treatment is to give students a chance to learn.

The possibility of two different ways of defining a social work role is recognized.

1. Harold L. Wilensky and Charles N. Lebeaux, *Industrial Society and Social Welfare* (New York: Russell Sage Foundation, 1958), pp. 289-91.
2. See Alvin W. Gouldner, "Cosmopolitans and Locals: Toward an Analysis of Latent Social Roles," *Administrative Science Quarterly*, II (1958), 281-306.

You can define it in terms of service and what social work traditionally does. But I personally justify what I do in terms of what
the unit's aims are. You can justify it either way. I know, I differ from the other social workers on this.

Consequently, the local is "not nearly as service oriented" as
other social workers.

Take _____; she is completely service oriented. This is
all she wants to do. I'm not like her. The way I see the social
worker's role in direct service is that it doesn't add up to a drop
in the bucket with all the psychiatrists and medical trainees
around here.

Because of her consideration for the educational needs of the
Department, the local sees her role primarily as a consultant for
psychiatric trainees, rather than as casework treatment.

I do as much collaborative treatment as I can, in addition to acting as consultant for all the trainees. I think a social worker can
make a bigger contribution in this area [consulting] than in a
service [treatment] area.

Regarding the consulting function, she concentrates on informing psychiatric trainees—especially medical students—about
welfare agencies, follow-up treatment agencies, state hospitals,
and other agencies available for the trainee's use in his treatment
of patients. In formal teaching sessions with medical students,
she realizes that medical students "don't care anything about
listening to a social worker," but "you've got to expect this."
Medical students are not going to consider a social work class
"an invaluable class" because "they're medical students, not social
work students." Therefore, rather than instructing them about
what social work "is" and "does," the local concentrates on informing them "about the psychiatric resources in the state": what
the various state institutions have in the way of psychiatric service, social workers, and the psychiatric facilities that are needed.
"Here again," she states, "I'm different from the other social
workers."

Educational needs are further emphasized in her performance
of casework services. She works mostly with medical students
rather than residents, "primarily because the resident is better
able to function alone than the medical students." She emphasizes
medical student education, even though she prefers to work with

residents. "It's more fun working with residents" because they are more skilled and advanced and, therefore, "treatment can be more intensive."

With the exception of one other cosmopolitan, the local differs from other social workers in that she expresses an interest in, and devotes time to, research. "I like this. I guess I'm just funny. I don't know why [I like research]; I'm just curious, I guess."

The local is different from the cosmopolitans not only in terms of role definition, but in experiencing no difficulty working with residents. Also, along with one cosmopolitan, she makes no reference to a problem of prestige: In interviews, she never refers to problems of faculty status, higher salaries, a lack of "status," or being respected as a professional and as a "colleague" by psychiatrists. In fact, she considers the Department an "ideal setting" in which to work: "I really am happy with my job here." In addition, she states that she is "not as concerned [as other social workers] with getting a corner on the market in service areas. I think it's futile to try to fight out areas of patient care." Consequently, there is a lack of concern with psychiatric trainees performing "traditional social work functions."

> I have not focused on in-take. A lot of social workers think that we should perform this function. I disagree. I think that this should be performed by the psychiatric trainees so they will have the experience. After all, this is why we are all here. The primary function of the Department is education and that should be given first consideration. I concentrate on seeing how I can help here instead of fighting out service areas. I know, I may be different— my viewpoint on this is different from most social workers. But this is not a social work agency; this is a medical setting and, well, I guess I'm just different about this.

The local's various references to being "different" from the other social workers[3] are certainly borne out when compared to the others' role definition, their problems with residents, and their prestige deprivation. This suggests a possible relationship between role definition and these two problems.

In connection with the local's lack of difficulty working with

---

3. In this connection she made the following statements in reference to being "happy with my job here": "I guess I sound a little crazy. . . . There must be something wrong with me."

residents, it is important to note that her interest is not primarily casework. For example:

> I think I should have been a sociologist, really. I have a lot of interest in research and I'm interested in sociology. The others are more completely service oriented than I am.

The local, as she says, is not "so much concerned with social work itself as the others." The lack of interest in casework, along with more interest in medical students, reveals that she does not work with residents as much as the others, which may explain why she has less difficulty working with them. There is no structural reason for this difference: to work on cases with residents, the local too depends on referral from residents. In any case, she expresses no difficulty working with residents, whereas all cosmopolitans do.

More important in terms of this chapter is the association between role definition and problems of prestige. The local states: "I guess I'm not a real good professional social worker. I'm not so much concerned with what social work functions are, and what its status as a profession is." This suggests that concern for greater "status" is related to the way social workers define their role.

The previous chapter indicates that the social workers' concern with the psychiatrists' evaluation of them has reference to their performance of a psychotherapeutic role: They want to be recognized and respected as capable of performing "a form of psychotherapy," which in turn is associated with being seen as knowledgeable and competent professionals. There is also the rejection of the welfare role and a tendency to dissociate this from "professional status." [4] A distinction within the cosmopolitans supports the hypothesis that differences in role definition along the welfare worker-"psychotherapist" dimension is related to prestige deprivation.

COSMOPOLITANS: "PSYCHIATRIC" SOCIAL WORKER AND
SOCIAL WORKER "IN" PSYCHIATRY

As noted above, the work of Wilensky and Lebeaux points out that casework is the dominant specialty in social work. The authors also indicate that the history of casework is characterized

4. See pp. 166-67 above.

by two emphases. Originally, casework emphasized "environmental manipulation" (housing, financial assistance, vocational rehabilitation, etc.); but this has been replaced with an emphasis on casework as a "type of counseling process" where the "resemblance to psychotherapy is close." [5] It is in terms of these two different emphases that the cosmopolitans will be distinguished.

In reference to the social workers' rejection of the "welfare" worker role, there is one member who states: "I'm peculiar. I'm a social worker in psychiatry rather than a psychiatric social worker. The difference in emphasis is a little thing, but it is important. Some of the others don't see it that way." What the respondent means by being "peculiar" is in reference to the way she defines the social work role.

> I went through the period of wanting to treat people only, and wanted to be accepted by psychiatry as one who did treat emotionally disturbed people. [But] I began to see that I didn't need to prove that to them. It's senseless to compete with them. I feel that a social worker has more to offer than just treating people. We are concerned with more than just this. At first I didn't want to be seen as an environment manipulator—like the public sees us, like someone to get financial aid. I wanted them [psychiatrists] to see me as more than just an environmental manipulator. I wanted to be a little more dignified than this, you might say. Social work does treat people, but we do more than that. I'm truer to social work if I show them [psychiatrists] that social work does more than treatment per se. Some of the others aren't like this. ——————— is at the other extreme—she wants to be a junior psychiatrist. She would be ashamed to say that she is concerned with environmental manipulation—vocational rehabilitation and welfare and getting patients in nursing homes. I want to be seen as a professional person who performs a treatment role, sure. But more. I want them to see me as someone who treats people, but I don't want them to have a limited concept of social work. Social work is neither one nor the other. Some of the others want to be accepted only as someone who treats.

These comments suggest that the social worker's role definition is related to the way she wants to be seen and accepted by psychiatrists. Accordingly, the above respondent is the only social worker, other than the local, who never expressed dissatisfaction or concern in interviews about faculty status, salary, "status," or

5. Wilensky and Lebeaux, *Industrial Society and Social Welfare*, p. 289.

psychiatrists' evaluation of social workers.[6] The implication is that when a social worker incorporates a welfare orientation into his or her role conception, there is less concern with prestige, insofar as prestige is dependent upon psychiatrists' attitudes. For example, the social worker "in" psychiatry has not "thought much about" faculty status, and is "not too concerned about it right now, and [has not] been." This respondent's comments about another social worker,[7] who is concerned about social workers' prestige problems, also points to a possible relationship between role definition and the need for greater prestige.

> I think _____ wants to be a psychiatrist more than a social worker. She identifies with psychiatry, not social work. But what I think of her is, well, she is just a social climber.

The suggestion that there is a relationship between role definition and prestige deprivation receives crude support from responses to the first interview question asked of each social worker. Excluding the local who has an entirely different role conception, six social workers were asked: "As a psychiatric social worker, what are your functions in the Department, and who are the persons with whom you perform them?"[8] Only two mentioned a welfare function;[9] on this basis, both are tentatively classified as emphasizing a welfare dimension in the social work role. The psychiatric social worker "in" psychiatry is one of the two. The other, later in the same interview, expressed displeasure at being seen in a welfare role. On the other hand, the social worker "in" psychiatry indicates a desire to be seen in the role of welfare worker. On the basis of these criteria, all other social workers, including the one who mentioned the performance of welfare functions, are classified as social workers who emphasize a therapeutic role to the exclusion of a welfare role. They will be referred to as "psychiatric" social workers or "psychiatric" cos-

6. Although, as noted in the previous chapter, the supervisor's position is ambiguous.
7. Who, in terms of criteria to be employed shortly, does not incorporate a welfare orientation into the psychiatric social worker's role.
8. The psychiatric social work supervisor was not asked this question. However, he agrees with the "psychiatric" cosmopolitans that the "primary" social work role is one of casework treatment with the family and concern with "family pathology" and "family interaction" and how these have a bearing on the patient's illness.
9. Welfare functions that were mentioned include "economic assistance," "vocational rehabilitation," "housing," and "schooling."

mopolitans. The lone social worker expressing a desire to be seen as an "environment manipulator" will be referred to as a social worker "in" psychiatry.

The fact that the social worker "in" psychiatry and the local are the only ones who do not refer to the problems of prestige is, of course, only a crude indication that a relationship exists between role conception and prestige deprivation. In addition, the conclusion that there is a relationship rests heavily on what the social worker "in" psychiatry says about the relative importance of welfare services and treating "emotionally disturbed people." Nevertheless, differences between this social worker and other cosmopolitans in their evaluation of an administrative change which resulted in the merger of the psychiatric and medical social work groups support the hypothesis.

INTEGRATION OF THE PSYCHIATRIC AND MEDICAL SOCIAL WORK GROUPS

Unlike psychology and recreation, social workers do not have a close relationship with their corresponding campus department. No social worker has an appointment in the university Department of Social Work; the two groups are separated ideologically in that each has a different "philosophy" of social work, the campus department being of the Rankian or "functional" school with the psychiatric group adhering to the Freudian or "diagnostic" school.[10] According to the psychiatric social work supervisor, the difference in "philosophy" is a major reason for a lack of contact between the two groups. The supervisor, who thinks the university department would send more of their students to the psychiatric unit for training purposes if there were a closer relationship between them, maintains that it does not "bother" him "too much," since he is able to get students "from plenty of other schools."

In addition, before they were integrated with medical social workers from nonpsychiatric areas of the hospital, psychiatric social workers were administratively separate from other hospital social workers. There was a separate supervisor for each group, with the psychiatric social work supervisor being administratively responsible to the Chairman of the Department of Psychiatry.

10. On the distinction between Rankian (functional) casework and Freudian (diagnostic) casework, see Cora A. Kasius, *A Comparison of Diagnostic and Functional Casework Concepts* (New York: Family Service Association of America, 1950).

Consequently, there was no other group with whom members of the psychiatric social workers had formal colleague relationships. The merger of the psychiatric and medical social work groups, which was preceded by the elimination of the position of psychiatric social work supervisor following his resignation, eliminated this. The psychiatric group then became administratively responsible to the over-all social work supervisor—a medical social worker.

To the extent that psychiatric social workers identify with the general profession of social work, their approval of the change would be anticipated. However, the new supervisor reports that they did not want integration and were not happy with it. Interviews with the psychiatric social workers reveal that most, but not all, were against the merger. Before discussing this, some differences between the psychiatric and medical groups should be noted.

Until the change went into effect and the over-all director arrived, the psychiatric group's salaries were somewhat higher than the medical group's. Through the actions of the director, the latter salaries were raised so that a uniform pay scale prevailed. Another difference was the possession of a private office by each member of the psychiatric group, whereas the medical workers shared offices. Finally, although no study was made of the medical group, one psychiatric social worker, who at one time had been a member of the medical group, stated that the latter group was mostly concerned with welfare and financial aid to patients, whereas the psychiatric group was mostly concerned with a treatment role.

In all, six psychiatric social workers were interviewed concerning their views of the merger. The cosmopolitans' views will be discussed first.

COSMOPOLITANS AND INTEGRATION

Four cosmopolitans were against the change[11] and one was for

11. Two gave an unqualified "against" and one gave an unqualified "for" in response to the question: "How do you feel about integration, are you for it or against it?" Another answered, "It's sort of like asking someone who's been an independent liberal for a long time how they like being a Republican." The fourth replied that it was "too early to tell." However, the relative advantages and disadvantages of the merger perceived by the last subject definitely place her in the "against" category. In addition, the writer was informed by another social worker that this subject was definitely against the merger.

it—the one for it being the social worker "in" psychiatry. In discussing their "against" positions, "psychiatric" cosmopolitans refer to the difference between psychiatric and medical social work. Three claim that they perform more of a treatment function than medical social workers. For example, one states that medical social workers are more likely to be "oriented to the environment" and "to things like vocational rehabilitation," whereas psychiatric social workers are "more oriented to a therapist function." The fourth argues that the practice between medical and psychiatric social work is different because the latter works "altogether with psychological material."

The perceived differences in role between psychiatric and medical social workers lead these four to see the two groups as different and separate groups, as is indicated by their "against" position. In addition, three mention the uniform pay scale unfavorably. Two refer to it as a loss, and one states that it creates recruitment problems because "you can't get good psychiatric social workers for what you pay medical social workers."

On the other hand, the social worker "in" psychiatry sees no difference in the two roles, although she realizes that "a lot of them over there still are handmaidens to doctors—they take his phone calls, write his letters, run his errands, etc." Still there is no difference in role because "this shouldn't be."

> Social work is social work wherever he or she may work. The setting may be different—our setting is different from over there—but we use the same tools, you might say. We have the same knowledge and skills whether we work in psychiatry, medical, or child clinics. We operate on the same principles, although the language is a little different. We talk more in psychiatric terms than they do, but that's the only difference. We are different only in terms of the setting.

Not only are no differences seen between medical and psychiatric social work, but no distinction is made between any of the social work specialties.

> Basically, a social worker is a social worker wherever you find him or her—the same skills and knowledge are used; all are concerned with casework. A social worker is a social worker whether he or she works in a juvenile court, a welfare agency, community clinic, or a hospital. The only difference is the setting.

Like the other social workers, this one also notes a difference between the salaries of the two specialties (along with better working conditions), but again feels that "this shouldn't be."

There is evidence that the different cosmopolitan orientations are associated with differences in group identifications. This is explicit in the case of the social worker "in" psychiatry.

> The way I feel about [the merger] is this: if anyone asks me what I do, I don't say I'm a psychiatric social worker, but a social worker in the Psychiatry Department here. My loyalty is to the Social Work Department first, then to the Psychiatry.

On the other hand, a "psychiatric" social worker, in commenting on a social work position that had recently been taken away from the psychiatric group, stated:

> But, then, there are none in some medical specialties. I'm all for their getting them; I think that they should have them and I hope they get them. But who's going to push for us? They need social workers, sure, but our concern is here.

It was our argument above that the expressive orientations of the two types of social workers were different: the social worker "in" psychiatry is less concerned with prestige than the "psychiatric" social workers. It was further argued that in their orientation toward greater prestige, the "psychiatric" social workers were strongly oriented to psychiatrists' appraisal of them. The differential assessment of the relative advantages and disadvantages of the merger, as seen by two "psychiatric" social workers[12] and the social worker "in" psychiatry, is consistent with this thesis. The advantages and disadvantages will be discussed in terms of the relative instrumental (work) and expressive advantages and disadvantages perceived.

Instrumental Advantages and Disadvantages Perceived

No one mentioned any instrumental disadvantage. However, both "psychiatric" cosmopolitans mentioned the advantage of having a central patient index, but one had doubts if it would work since "our work is so different from theirs." In addition, one mentioned the possible advantage of rotating social workers from

12. Only two of the four "psychiatric" social workers were interviewed specifically regarding the relative advantages and disadvantages of integration.

one group to the other for short periods when one group experiences a shortage, and the other mentioned the possibility of a better co-ordinated teaching program.

Expressive Advantages and Disadvantages Perceived

Before the merger, the psychiatric social workers, because of their administrative affiliation with the Department of Psychiatry, enjoyed the advantage of higher salaries, as well as expense money to attend professional conferences and conventions. With the merger, these privileges no longer separated the two groups. The "psychiatric" social workers felt these things were lost; the social worker "in" psychiatry felt that nothing was lost, but that much was gained.

In speaking of the advantages of integration, the social worker "in" psychiatry states that social workers are "stronger" and that it has helped both the medical and psychiatric groups. Psychiatric social workers are stronger because previously they were "affiliated with psychiatry [and] moved along with psychiatry. Before, we were completely dependent on psychiatry. Now we aren't. We are a separate department."

What they were dependent on psychiatry for and the way the respondent felt about it are revealed in the following:

> Social Worker: Well, for everything. Things like office space, salary—they didn't have the complete say-so here [salary], but for the most part they did—but everything. What we got, psychiatry dictated it. I'm not saying it's been bad for us. In fact, it's been good. We had higher salaries for a while, we got money to go to meetings, money to attend conferences, and probably would have gotten our national dues paid. We got all of these things but the others [medical social workers] couldn't.

> Interviewer: Seems like you are saying that integration is a disadvantage rather than an advantage.

> Social Worker: It does seem like a disadvantage, doesn't it? But I would rather not have them than to have to get them from psychiatry, and not be integrated with medical social work.

Although material rewards are lost, they can be forgone because of social rewards gained. The former are the price of the latter. The "psychiatric" cosmopolitans consider these privileges their right as "professional people." It is not that the social worker "in" psychiatry has an image that is less professional than the others; only that she fails to associate the same social rewards with these benefits that the others do. For her, these material rewards do not have an additional increment of social reward. They do have this increment for "psychiatric" cosmopolitans. They are prestige symbols.

Before discussing the expressive disadvantages, it should be mentioned that both "psychiatric" cosmopolitans feel that a possible advantage of integration is the opportunity to "identify" with a larger professional group, although one sees this as something of a problem.

> Of course, we identify with social work first, but we are also closely related to psychiatrists, and identify with the Psychiatry Department. As more social workers are hired this may change, I don't know. But it's a transition in our identifications that is hard to make.

Analysis of the expressive disadvantages mentioned by the two social workers reveals why the "transition in identifications" is hard to make.

Regarding salary differentials, the two "psychiatric" social workers were not concerned merely with the amount of pay that differentiated the two groups, but *what the differences symbolized*. One states that psychiatric social workers have "advanced greater in terms of professional status, training, and self-awareness of our contribution in medical settings than medical social workers"; this "has been recognized" in the form of higher salaries. However, "recently, their classification and salary was changed to the same as ours. Now we are all the same. Now our budgeted position has been taken away from us." Not only higher salaries, but other symbols of recognition differentiated psychiatric and medical social workers.

> One possible advantage [of having a separate group] is that social work is a more integrated part of psychiatry and is accepted by psychiatry, than it is in, say, surgery. Because of that, they recognize us as a professional group with professional skills. When I came here, I expected a private office; _____ recognized this. I had to have a private office to talk about intimate things with clients; _____ recognized this. Over there, they don't.

Interestingly, the mere fact of integration had no effect on whether psychiatric social workers had private offices. The social worker simply does not want to be *associated* with another group which does not receive "professional recognition" (conveyed through the symbol of private offices) from the medical profession.

The above response also reveals the function a symbol like private offices may perform in giving the "psychiatric" social worker a feeling of professional recognition and acceptance. She implies, however, that the value of this symbol is actually *lost* (i.e., it is no longer an advantage) when psychiatric and medical social workers are integrated. This is explicitly the case for salary differentials: the value of salary as a prestige symbol is lost when others who formerly had a lower salary are raised to your salary, especially when you are placed in the same group with them. When medical social workers are granted salaries equal to those of the "psychiatric" social workers, the latter suffers a loss. The loss is not an absolute monetary one, however, for the uniform pay scale resulted from the medical group's salary being elevated. The loss is felt because pay differentials symbolize differentials in the way one is evaluated in terms of "professional status," "training," and "awareness" of one's contribution." It is expressive deprivation—but relative deprivation rather than absolute deprivation. Relative to another group, the "psychiatric" social workers suffered a loss since the "lower" group (the less "professional") gained.

In other instances, the "psychiatric" social workers' loss is not relative to what the medical social workers receive. For example, without integration,

> we're closer to our department people and can get things we need and attention. For instance, psychiatrists get so much expenses for such things as going to conferences, etc., then psychologists got them, so social workers said, Why not us? _____ [Department head] said, okay, why not. Now we are tied to what they [medical social workers] get.

Nevertheless, psychologists represent a comparative reference group to determine what the social workers think they have a right to receive.

The social-psychological function of this privilege, being a symbol of professional acceptance and recognition, is brought out even more explicitly by the other "psychiatric" social worker.

It used to be the general policy of the department, at least I think it was the general policy, that psychologists and social workers' expenses to conferences would be paid, up to $200. Also, if you were giving a paper or were on an executive committee, your expenses were paid. This means something to me personally; just to get away for a few days and see people, if nothing else. I think it's understandable that we don't want these things taken away from us. This has been a source of gratification to us—I think that's understandable. We feel that we make a professional contribution; we don't want things taken away from us that we feel we are entitled to as professional people. . . . This is a source of recognition that is gratifying to us, but this has now been taken away. I think it's understandable why we feel this way [not liking integration].

Thus, if the "psychiatric" social workers felt deprived before being integrated with medical social workers, they are even more deprived as a result of it. In this connection, additional light is thrown on the expressive role of the departed supervisor. For example, "I think psychologists are going to get their national dues paid. If _____ [departed supervisor] were still here, he would have been able to get this for social work." With integration this is not possible. In addition, integration means that the head of the Department of Psychiatry "can't get us vacation, academic status, any more" because "everything is out of his hands."

The structural change reveals still another side of the departed supervisor's role. Formerly,

if we had a problem, we could tell him about it and he could take it from there. We had this direct line to _____ [Department head], and we had identification with the Psychiatry Department—we could identify with the Department. Now we don't. We have no way to identify with the Department any more. This relationship has been broken off.

The social worker works in the same setting with the same persons, yet things are different without the supervisor. With him as the "link" to the psychiatrists, the "psychiatric" social workers are able to associate themselves with the Department of Psychiatry. A "weak" and "incompetent" supervisor, who, because of the position he occupied, allowed social workers to "identify" with the Department of Psychiatry, is better than no supervisor.

THE LOCAL AND INTEGRATION

Although the two types of cosmopolitans take different positions on integration, they are similar in that both have definite and unambiguous opinions about it. In contrast, the local's position is one of equivocation. In reply to the question regarding the relative advantages of each, the local states: "There would be advantages to both, I suppose." Probing this response brought the following replies.

Integration is seen to have the instrumental advantage of facilitating the transfer of patients between the Department of Psychiatry and other medical departments. "For professional reasons," however, the local thinks "it might be best to have a separate group," although "administratively it makes more sense to have one department." The local's straddling the issue is clearly seen in the following statements.

> [Integration would be advantageous for] things like salary and your rank in the hospital. Conceivably, I can see these things being easier if you have more power—you would have more power to get things like better salaries, I suppose. There are more in the group; there would be more in terms of numbers, if this is anything power-wise. Oh, it's just silly to be separate in an administrative sense. But from a selfish point of view it might work best to be separate. Psychiatric social work is given much more of a professional role than are medical social workers. Over here the social worker is more involved in the treatment process. It's just a difference in the way they use your services. [In medical social work the social worker is more likely to be seen in something akin to a welfare worker role.]

In evaluating integration, the local mentions some of the same things that the cosmopolitans do: salary, academic rank, the association between professional status and performing a treatment role, and the way medical social work is evaluated by the medical profession. However, unlike the cosmopolitans, she fails to take a definite stand. When forced, she finally takes a position, but one that compromises the "psychiatric" social workers' and the social worker "in" psychiatry's positions.

Interviewer: Could you say that you are for or against it?

Local: As an organization person I am for it. It's sensible; it's not sensible to have a separate unit. But for the unit—the social workers in the psychiatric unit—it would probably be better to have a separate unit. Boy, that's a really wishy-washy answer, isn't it?

Interviewer: You say it would be better for the social workers in the psychiatric unit to remain separate. But how about you as an individual? If it were up to you to decide, on which side of the fence would you be?

Local: I'm not discontented with it like it is. But I would probably say, separate. Let me put it this way. I would prefer an over-all group but a psychiatric social work supervisor who is _____'s [over-all director's] administrative assistant.

Several things stand out here. First, the local finds it difficult to be decisive and, when pressed, gives a "wishy-washy answer." Second, although integration is seen as a possible disadvantage for the psychiatric social work unit, the local—as an individual —never indicates strong involvement in the issue. Third, unlike the social worker "in" psychiatry, the local is not definitely for integration; but, unlike the "psychiatric" social workers, she is not discontented with it either. All of this reveals that the local, who "guesses," "I'm not a real good professional social worker," is not "concerned as much with social work as some of the rest," as well as "what its status as a profession is." Consequently, if the local had the power to decide for or against integration, she would "probably" be against, but a compromise is preferred—a position midway between the "psychiatric" social workers and the social worker "in" psychiatry. This position would make psychiatric social work separate from, yet integrated with, medical social work.

PROPOSED STRUCTURAL CHANGE AND THE INCOMPATIBILITY OF INSTRUMENTAL AND EXPRESSIVE ORIENTATIONS

Although integration conflicted with the "psychiatric" social workers' expressive orientations, it had little or no effect on their instrumental role performance, insofar as casework duties and working with residents were concerned. However, the analysis of the recreation service and clinical psychology revealed that under certain conditions an instrumental need may be in conflict with an expressive need. In this section, conflicting requirements of instrumental and expressive orientations will be discussed in reference to a proposed structural change.

In Chapter 5, we described the social workers' need for a closer working relationship with senior psychiatrists in order to control the residents' behavior. In the last chapter, we saw that social workers do not want just any relationship, i.e., they do not want a particularistic relationship, because of their expressive orientations. In this section, data will reveal a conflict between the two objectives.

Shortly after the termination of the meetings between the three psychiatrists and the social workers,[13] the psychiatric administration proposed that social workers be assigned to individual psychiatrists under whom they worked. For example, inpatient social workers would be assigned to the attending man on individual wards, rather than to the psychiatric social work supervisor. At this time the latter position was abolished. Since this is the only aspect of the proposal that was realized, observation of the effects of the proposed change was not possible. However, it was possible to determine how social workers would feel about such a change in the event it were put into operation.

On the surface, there is reason to expect the social workers' approval. In terms of their instrumental role, it would appear to be an acceptable solution for some of their difficulties with the residents, since it would give them closer working relationships with the staff psychiatrists, the residents' superior. However, the questioning of six social workers indicates strong disapproval of the proposal.

Of the six, one "psychiatric" cosmopolitan states that it would not be "feasible or possible." She works with so many different psychiatrists it would be a problem as to whom she would be assigned; therefore, it is altogether a "theoretical question." The remaining five express definite disapproval. Different reasons are given, and these, in turn, are related to local-cosmopolitan differences, as well as to differences within the cosmopolitans.

Three social workers voice a certain ambivalence toward the change. In each case the ambivalence derives from a conflict between instrumental and expressive orientations. One "psychiatric" social worker, who is against the change because "we are a separate profession," also says:

13. See p. 60 above.

If anything peculiar comes up, the social worker can go to the psychiatrist and get it settled. At one time the residents were particularly hostile, we felt; we were having a difficult time working with them. We went to _____ [psychiatrist in charge of the service unit] and he gave us some backing. He talked to the supervising psychiatrists about our problems, and apparently they talked with the residents.

The social worker "in" psychiatry also thinks the change would be a help when residents fail to co-operate because there would be "a need to take it to [the psychiatrist] and try to get him to do something about getting the residents to use us." Nevertheless, the change is not desired: "I feel that I'm a member of the Social Work Department as a whole—I feel no allegiance to psychiatry, but to social work. We are a separate department. We work in a psychiatric setting, but we should be independent of psychiatry." Preference is for assignment to an over-all hospital social work department, responsible to an over-all social work director.

A third social worker, a "psychiatric" social worker, thinks the proposal would work out best because the senior psychiatrist "has more authority in the department" than the social work supervisor, but she is against it "because of the self-image."

Social Worker: I don't want to be assigned to an individual staff man because we are social workers—a different profession. We're a different profession. But personally I think it would have worked out better if we had been assigned to an individual staff psychiatrist.

Interviewer: Why?

Social Worker: Because we could go to him to settle things and get problems straightened out. But I would be bitter because of the self-image.

. . . .

Social Worker: [The psychiatrist] has more authority in the Department than the social work director [had]. Also, I have a very good relationship with him and he understands what I can do.

Interviewer: What effect would it have on your self-image?

Social Worker: Because I would be assigned to an individual psychiatrist, not to a social work director. I would rather be seen as a member of the social work group than as a social worker on Ward X. If I'm assigned to a psychiatrist, I won't be defined as a social worker, but as a social worker on Ward X. I would rather be identified as a member of social work than as a social worker on Ward X.

Interviewer: Why?

Social Worker: Because of the self-image. People wouldn't see me as a member of the social work group.

Interviewer: But you think that perhaps there would be advantages to being assigned to an individual psychiatrist?

Social Worker: Yes. Things would work out better in that I could go to him and get problems settled.

Interviewer: Is this what you are saying: insofar as social work is concerned—the actual work involved in carrying out social work duties—it would be better if you were assigned individually to staff psychiatrists, but in terms of the image—the way you see yourself and the way others see you—the over-all psychiatric social worker supervisor is better? Is this correct?

Social Worker: It's funny, but it seems to be it.

Only when we realize that the social worker experiences difficulty in working with residents, as well as having a need to be seen as a professional person, is this "funny" situation understood.

The local is also against the proposed change, but for different reasons. The change would be all right with her "personally," since she and the psychiatrist (unit head) for whom she works "get along beautifully." As a general policy, however, "it would not be a good idea" because "it puts things on a personal basis, not a professional basis." Social workers would be "completely subject to [the] power" of the psychiatrist.

Because that way there would be no social work group—there would only be social workers assigned to individual psychiatrists. Therefore, the social worker wouldn't have any power because this [group] is the only power an ancillary group has.

What the social worker means in her reference to "power" is the problem of who would define the social work role—the psychiatrist or the social worker. For,

personally it would work out okay for me. _____ and I agree completely on my role. But it would be too dangerous as a general policy. It would be too much like a dictatorship—you are too dependent on the benevolence of the psychiatrist. What he wants you to do, you do. But I wouldn't mind it with _____ because we agree on what I'm to do.

Interviewer: Then you, personally, wouldn't be against it for any reason if there is agreement on what your role is?

Social Worker: As long as we agree on my role, it would be okay.

In opposing the proposed change, the local is in agreement with the cosmopolitans. Yet there is a basic difference, since personally she would not mind. The difference between her position and that of the cosmopolitans can best be seen when the local's responses are compared to the cosmopolitan immediately preceding.

Both the local and the cosmopolitan state that each individually has a good relationship with her supervising psychiatrist regarding her respective social work duties. Still, the cosmopolitan opposes the change because she wants to be seen as a member of a social work group. Individual acceptance does not confirm her self-image as a professionally competent person; only when she is seen as a member of a social work group is this image confirmed. In other words, the cosmopolitan's self-image is invested in the social work *group* and in a universalistic norm. Before she can be seen as a competent and knowledgeable social worker, other social workers must also be seen as such. Putting the senior psychiatrist-social worker relationship on an individual one-to-one basis precludes that.[14]

The local does not see herself as "a real good professional social worker," nor as one who is concerned with the status of social work as a profession. There is less investment of a self-image in the social work group. Consequently, she is willing to be treated particularistically: "Personally," the proposed change "would work out okay for me." To the extent that she is accepted in the role that she wants to play, "as long as [she and the psychiatrist] agree on [her] role, it would be okay."

Finally, one "psychiatric" social worker is against the proposal for both reasons given by the preceding two social workers:

14. This is the same social worker who had previously indicated dissatisfaction about the social work *group* not being accepted, although the supervising psychiatrist accepts "What *I* do." See p. 170 above.

the danger of being dependent on psychiatrists for role definition and not being seen as a member of a social work group. She feels that with this change the psychiatrist would "decapitate us."

Social Worker: It makes us impotent. Then we're not organized. If they keep us from being organized, keep us diffuse, we have to take what comes along.

Interviewer: You mean you have to do what they want, something like that?

Social Worker: That's right. Then we are at their mercy—what they want we have to do. That's why psychiatry always yells about psychologists. They are organized, that's why. Oh, we talk to each other informally, we see each other in the hall, and I know the other workers, but we don't have much contact. I feel like we are just individuals floating around. Individuals—not a social work group. We will see each other in the hall and that's about it.

Interviewer: You say that if you are assigned to an individual psychiatrist and are kept from having a psychiatric social work director you are at their mercy. What do you mean?

Social Worker: It's just common sense. We'll have to take anything that comes along. Whatever they want us to do, we do. There's an old saying, "in unity there's strength." As long as we are organized, there are no problems. Oh, there'll be problems; there always are, but they aren't as great. The primary dissatisfaction of the workers here comes in not being a unified group.

Unless social workers are seen as a group, their professional self-images are indeed in danger of "decapitation."

SOCIAL WORK: A PROFESSION?

Implied in much of the above is the suggestion that, as social workers become cosmopolitan oriented on an instrumental level, they tend to become oriented to the Department (psychiatry) on the expressive level. That is to say, as they define their role in terms of the professional standards of casework and as they emphasize the counseling or psychotherapeutic aspects of case work —and, in this sense, as they are oriented away from the Department—they are attracted to the Department. For example, those social workers who differentiate their role from that of medical social workers in terms of therapeutic skills prefer to remain members of the Department of Psychiatry, rather than be members of a hospital Department of Social Work.

The problem can be viewed in terms of reference groups. The profession of psychiatric social work functions as a normative reference group while the profession of psychiatry functions as an evaluative reference group. The social work profession provides the norms and values which the "psychiatric" social workers utilize in defining their role. Psychiatrists, on the other hand, have the power to deprive them of role confirmation, or to reward them through confirmation. It is true that their professional self-images are invested in a social work group—they must be seen as members of a group—but these images are also anchored in the group of psychiatrists, for it is they upon whom "psychiatric" social workers are dependent for self-image confirmation.

At this juncture it is relevant to ask: why are "psychiatric" cosmopolitans so dependent on psychiatrists? An answer to this question will provide us with considerations on the status of social work as a profession.

We have noted that social workers do not want just any kind of relationship with psychiatrists. They do not want an individual relationship—a particularistic relationship, nor just a close working relationship. They want, instead, acceptance as members of a professional group, a group that psychiatrists think is capable of performing certain therapeutic activities. The need for such a relationship must be found at the level of social structure and role definition.

Different authors have mentioned various traits that characterize professions, traits which differentiate professions from other occupational groups.[15] The view taken in this book is that the most essential trait qualifying an occupation for professional status is the ability to claim exclusive possession of competence in a specified area.[16] Such competence requires a theoretical base of knowledge and special technical skills which are exclusive to the occupation. The "psychiatric" cosmopolitans have neither of these prerequisites.

In the performance of the casework treatment role, the technical skills employed—therapeutic interviewing skills—are those

15. See Morris L. Cogan, "Toward a Definition of Profession," *Harvard Educational Review*, XXIII (1953), 33-50.
16. Wilensky and Lebeaux, *Industrial Society and Social Welfare*, p. 284.

of the psychiatrist (as well as clinical psychologist, educational counselor, and minister, for that matter). In addition, the theoretical base and terminology employed by psychiatric social workers are psychiatric (psychoanalytic) in nature. In other words, their role, as social workers themselves define it, is not sufficiently differentiated from what psychiatrists do to give them a hard core of skills and knowledge which they can claim as their own exclusive "professional property."

For example, social workers refer to casework as casework *treatment*. The social worker-relative relationship is seen as a therapeutic one: "this is a therapeutic relationship about the patient's hospitalization," or a "form of psychotherapy." Six social workers were questioned on the differences between casework treatment and psychotherapy. None was clear how casework differs from what psychiatrists do. For example, one maintained, "Some casework relationships are very similar and the same as what the psychiatrists do." Some do differentiate between the two, since social workers do not deal with the "unconscious," whereas the psychiatrists do. Even here, however, one is of the "opinion that a good skilled social worker may give therapy similar to what psychiatrists and residents do." Whether social workers are capable of administering psychotherapy is not the issue. What is at issue are the sociological consequences of social workers' defining their role in terms of interviewing and psychotherapeutic skills, as working with "psychological material," and claiming that "although there are differences between social work and psychiatry, we speak the same language, we have the same techniques."

At the level of social structure, social workers have no exclusive right to intellectual and professional skills vis-à-vis psychiatry. The local perceives this, stating that it is a "funny thing," but "the social worker is in a very unusual position in a setting like this—in a psychiatric setting—because the things she is trained in, other personnel are trained in, also." For another, this is not a "funny thing"—it "places social work at a disadvantage."

> We don't have any esoteric tools. There is nothing much that we have that we don't share with psychiatry. The interview is our primary tool, but this is true of psychiatry, too. The techniques that social workers use and the techniques of psychiatrists are both from psychoanalytic psychiatry. We have this common base,

except our training is in casework. What we have and what we can do, well, the same thing is granted to psychiatry. There is an area of overlapping which psychiatrists here don't understand. [Goes on to indicate that psychotherapy is a "continuum."] Psychoanalysis is at one extreme. Rogers' type of counseling is at the other end, and social work is somewhere in the middle. Some distinguished psychiatrists accept the fact that social workers do a form of psychotherapy. But there are others who think we try to be junior psychiatrists. There's a lot of this attitude here. This influences the status of social work in this kind of setting.

It is significant to note that this respondent sees the "area of overlapping" as something the psychiatrists fail to realize, elsewhere labeling this "a form of escapism." Unperceived are the social workers' defining their role too far into psychiatry's "area of competence." Thus, the lack of "esoteric tools" which "influences the status of social work."

In light of this tendency to define the social workers' skills as similar to those of the psychiatrist, it is relevant to note that psychiatrists sometimes speak of social workers as "frustrated doctors" and as wanting to be "junior psychiatrists." One states: "They don't know what they are, what they want to do; they have no defined role. They want to be junior psychiatrists, but they can't."

A further consequence of so defining their role, one which must be understood at the social-psychological level, is that the "psychiatric" cosmopolitans' own evaluation of their professional self and status becomes very much dependent on the psychiatrists' evaluation of them. This is understandable since, after all, psychiatrists are a more skillful group, if length of training and over-all prestige are taken as indicators of skill. It then becomes understandable why, in a psychiatric setting, a psychiatric social worker may become quite strongly oriented to the organization as well as away from it. This can be understood, however, only when distinctions are made within the social workers, and when both expressive and instrumental orientations are recognized and seen in terms of the instrumental (normative) reference group function of the social work profession and the expressive (evaluative) reference group function of psychiatry.

A further consequence of "psychiatric" social workers' defining their role as they do is to be vulnerable to the psychiatrists' claim that psychiatrists can operate in what social workers con-

sider their area of competence. For example, a psychiatrist states
to social workers that their function is not to work with families
because he determines what a person's function is by asking himself, "Whom would I turn to and to nobody else but this person
for getting this job done?" He does not use social workers for
casework treatment: "I work my own families, or I could turn
to the residents." Whether psychiatrists and residents are competent to work with families is not the point. The point is since
social workers define their role as they do, the psychiatrist may
say he (and psychiatric trainees) can competently perform tasks
which social workers consider to be their particular competence.
In fact, the psychiatrist may prefer seeing the relative himself:
"I would rather do it [work with relatives] myself, except where
it is not practicable."

By working with families, or permitting residents to do so,
psychiatrists deny casework treatment to social workers as their
exclusive area of competence. This, in turn, deprives the latter of
professional respect—for to convey professional respect means
that one respects another for his *unique* skills. Social workers are
denied an exclusive function because they have not defined their
role so that the skills involved are essentially different from psychiatrists'. Social workers have no "esoteric tools." [17]

The above suggests that social workers may experience problems in a medical setting which they do not encounter in community clinics and family agencies. Although this problem was
not systematically explored, there would seem to be two related
explanations for it. One stems from the emphasis on resident
education and the social workers' inability to accept this—i.e.,
to accept the residents' right to perform "traditional social work
functions." The effect of the educational emphasis on the social
workers' role is illustrated by the head of one of the services in
the context of discussing the social worker's role in the Department.

> That's hard to answer—what their primary role is. They have
> several roles, but the most important is demonstration on a clini-
> cal basis [teaching residents through demonstration]. Tradition-
> ally in social work, they do in-take interviews and functional

17. Almost fifty years ago, Abraham Flexner pointed to the social worker's
lack of unique technical skills as the crucial problem in social work's qualifying for professional status. See Abraham Flexner, "Is Social Work a
Profession?" *School and Society*, I (1915), 901-11.

interviews with parents. Traditionally, her role is to treat the parents in collaboration with the psychiatrist who treats the child. In some places it is the social worker who will treat the child. But the role varies [in this setting]—it depends on the needs of the case. I can explain this in terms of teaching and research. In this center, teaching and research are top dogs. It's mostly teaching though. What this means is not that service is not good. What it means is that service is as good as possible but teaching residents is the most important. So, in the case of the social worker, the educational needs of the resident will determine what her role is. In some cases a resident may show that he is capable of doing it all. He may do in-take, see the child, interview the parent, and treat all the members of the family who are involved. He would do it all and the social worker wouldn't be used at all. We do this because of the importance of teaching residents. We want them to have experience in all these areas so they will know what's involved. When they complete their training, they will know what the social worker does and have some understanding of family problems and community problems that are involved in treating patients.

The psychiatrists' emphasis on resident education results in residents' performing "traditional social work functions." This is precisely what certain social workers complained about in the preceding chapter. It also underscores the point made above: because the social workers define their role as they do, they have no area of competence from which psychiatric trainees can be excluded.

Related to this is a "role reversal" which the social worker may encounter in medical settings. In her more traditional settings, e.g., child guidance clinics, the social worker is often the one who is in charge of the case and the psychiatrist is used in a consulting capacity. In a medical setting, the physician has greater control of the case and the social worker is used as a consultant and advisor. A child psychiatrist puts it the following way:

It's sort of confusing [to say what the social worker's role is]. It's a hard question to answer. Historically, what the social worker has historically done is not what she does here. Traditionally, she did in-take. Also, traditionally, she has been involved in diagnostic study proper and with casework with the parent, which involves essentially psychiatric therapy with the parent. Also, in the traditional child clinic the social worker has, in an administrative sense, been in charge of the case—she does the correspondence with the various agencies, is in touch with social agencies, treats the family, and so on. Now the doctor here does a lot of these things, while we use social workers in an advisory capacity.

In a medical setting the social worker is not as important—insofar as her traditional role is concerned—as she is in other settings. The local perceives this clearly. She also realizes that it derives from the educational emphasis of the Department and the need to "reverse" roles with the psychiatrist—to become a consultant.

So the medical students and residents do diagnostic interviews and interview relatives. Well, how else are they going to learn? They should have the opportunity to do these things. In a community clinic it would be a different story; here you have only one psychiatrist—as a consultant. Sure, the social workers will see all the relatives and do most of the treatment. But here it's absurd. I couldn't possibly see all relatives. Nor can the other services, with twenty-six therapists around the place, in addition to the trainees. So I have tried to see where social service could make the greatest contribution here in a consulting capacity. This is a medical school; concern is with medical education. So why shouldn't medical students and residents do in-take interviews? This is the only way they are going to learn these things, and it's important that they know these things. In the long run consulting is a service contribution. I focus on the students' education. Social service in a community clinic would be a different matter.

Being more important in their traditional settings, social workers probably have more prestige in these settings. We have argued above that the "psychiatric" social workers' source of prestige is the evaluation they receive from psychiatrists. If this hypothesis is valid, it should also hold for their more traditional settings. This is necessarily true because casework treatment skills are the same wherever the psychiatric social worker is employed. Whether in a community agency, child guidance center, mental health center, or a department of psychiatry, psychiatric social workers carry the same interviewing skills and psychoanalytic theoretical knowledge with them. Their role conception and professional self-image are transported from setting to setting. Consequently, we would expect their dependence on the evaluation and appraisal of psychiatrists in settings other than departments of psychiatry. There are, of course, no data to substantiate this assertion, but a social worker's comment is suggestive.

> Problems are created because of the emphasis on resident training here. We don't get as much reward as we would in other settings. There is no one psychiatrist as a papa figure patting you on the back telling you what a good job you are doing and what a good boy you are.

The respondent continues to point out that "in many settings the social worker is in much closer contact with the psychiatrist" than is true in the present setting.

Disregarding the psychoanalytic interpretation of the social worker-psychiatrist relationship, this comment reveals that social workers may often desire a close relationship with the psychiatrist in other settings, a desire based on other than purely instrumental (work) considerations. The respondent's psychoanalytic interpretation is, at best, not completely accurate, since it implies a particularistic relationship, one which is symbolic of parent-child relationships. The psychiatrist's symbolic significance to the social worker does not reside in his ability to play the role of father figure, but in his ability to reward her by conveying professional respect to her and, thereby, confirming her professional self-image.

Still to be explained is the social worker "in" psychiatry who indicates a lack of dependency on psychiatrists for the gratification of expressive orientations. This social worker also wants to "treat emotionally disturbed people" and, like the "psychiatric cosmopolitans," is not clear how casework treatment is differentiated from psychotherapy. However, social work is defined as capable of doing more than "treat emotionally disturbed people" —it is also very much concerned with welfare and economic assistance. The definition of this role is also taken from the professional standards of the social work profession, but it is such that no difference is seen between psychiatric social work and other kinds of social work. Accordingly, this social worker is attracted to a generalized profession of social work. Her attraction is reflected in the desire for the integration of psychiatric and medical social workers. There are no data which indicate why this social worker defines the social work role differently from the other cosmopolitans, however.

Interviewer: What do you think accounts for this difference between you and the other social workers?

Social Worker: I don't know. We have the same educational background. My allegiance is more to social work than to psychiatry.

In the case of the local, we saw where she defined her role as primarily an educational and consulting one. While this definition is based on organizational rather than professional considerations, it does not appear to have resulted from a need to please or to be accepted by psychiatrists. Paradoxically, the one social worker who most explicitly defines her role in terms of departmental objectives is also the one who is most explicit about not being concerned with the way she is appraised by psychiatrists, if the following statement can be taken as an indication of a lack of such concern—"I have no need for them [psychiatrists] to think I'm clever."

The question becomes: why does the local define her role differently? Since role definition is related to need for prestige, it is pertinent to note that the local is a middle-aged woman who is married to a university professor. Consequently, her prestige is not dependent on her status as a social worker. Because of this, and because she has only recently become a social worker, she probably has less invested in her status and career as a social worker than the "psychiatric" cosmopolitans. Both of these factors are mentioned by the local in reply to the following question, which followed her statement regarding the differences between the social work role in this setting and in community clinics, and her tendency to emphasize the educational or consulting aspects of her role.

Interviewer: You don't sound much like a dyed-in-the-wool social worker.

Social Worker: I'm beginning to wonder if that's not it. I'm not dependent on social work for my status, I guess. If I had become a social worker twenty years ago, I might look at things a little differently.

Having less investment in a professional self, she appears to have less need for self confirmation from psychiatrists.

SUMMARY AND CONCLUSIONS

Differences between social workers in terms of instrumental role definition were found to be related to expressed dissatisfaction with the psychiatrists' attitudinal evaluation of social work. Role definition also differentiated between social workers in terms of their evaluation of the integration of psychiatric and medical social work, as well as their evaluation of a proposed structural change. For some, the proposed change represented a conflict between instrumental and expressive considerations.

It was suggested that a major factor in the social workers' expressive deprivation resulted from the fact that—in a department of psychiatry at least—it is difficult for social workers to maintain a genuine professional position. Because their role definition overlaps into the psychiatrists' area of competence, what they consider to be their *unique* ability is not always accorded professional respect—e.g., psychiatric trainees are allowed to perform the social workers' "unique" tasks. Other factors besides role definition which were involved in social workers' expressive deprivation included the educational emphasis of the Department and the difference between the structure of medical settings and traditional social work agencies. It would appear that departments of psychiatry pose severe problems for "psychiatric" social workers' self confirmation.

Finally, on the basis of the local's responses, it was suggested that the differences in role definition may be due to dependence on social work status for prestige and to career contingencies.

A major finding of the chapter is the differential effect of the same structure, or changes (actual or proposed) in that structure, in creating expressive problems for social workers. The two who emphasize something other than the casework aspect of their role tend to encounter fewer problems of expressive deprivation. By showing the relationship between role definition and expressive deprivation, the chapter illustrates how instrumental and expressive orientations may become importantly intertwined in the orientations of individual actors.

12 CLINICAL PSYCHOLOGY AND PSYCHIATRIC SOCIAL WORK: A COMPARISON

The analysis of the social workers has indicated that psychiatrists are an important evaluative reference group for the "psychiatric" social workers. Data on the reporting phase of the psychologists' diagnostic role revealed that psychologists' complaints were similar to some of the social workers' complaints: a lack of respect, appreciation, and recognition for their work.[1] Seemingly, psychiatrists are important sources of expressive gratification for both psychologists and social workers. We will examine this problem in this chapter. Although the following data were not systematically collected for the purpose of comparing psychologists and social workers, and so are inconclusive because of this, they suggest that the psychiatrists' expressive power over the two groups is different.

The first thing to note is the difference between social workers and psychologists in their relationship with their campus counterparts. The alignment of the psychologists with the university Department of Psychology affords them an opportunity to engage

1. See chap. 9.

in teaching, very probably giving them greater prestige in the community by virtue of an academic appointment. It also gives at least some of them a feeling of support in their relations with the psychiatrists and the Department of Psychiatry. For example, four mention that they were supported by the Department of Psychology, which applied pressure on the Department of Psychiatry, once when psychiatrists tried to restrict the psychologist's psychotherapeutic activities. One speaks more generally of the support and power they receive from their campus department.

> The department on campus has helped us and saved our necks on occasion. We wouldn't have a chance in a power fight with them if we didn't have the department's backing. We want to do therapy but some time back they tried to cut this out. We feel that they wanted to keep us responsible to them. . . . We might need more office space. We can't demand it. We can yell about it, but if they don't want to give it to us they don't have to. Then we go to the campus and they help us out. . . . If they are pulling the string too tight on us, we go to the campus. They tell them [psychiatrists] that they need an intern program for their students. They [psychiatrists] say, but we need a residency program. The psychologists will say, but you can't have it without psychologists there—we'll pull out. They tell us in the department [on campus] that we need them and they need us, and to keep it that way—a sort of symbiosis. We fight it out with them until they try to pull the string as tight as they can. Then we go to the department on campus.

The validity of these statements—how much power the Department of Psychology has over the Department of Psychiatry and the power dynamics between the two—is not known as this particular problem was not investigated. For our purposes, it is only relevant to note that the psychologists' alignment with their campus department gives them a sense of support and power. If nothing else, it gives them a feeling that they have a source of power to turn to when it is needed. This reveals a basic difference between the psychologists and social workers. In speaking of the support psychologists receive from their campus department, one psychologist remarks:

> If it weren't for the Psychology Department on the campus, we would be at their mercy. This is where we are different from social work—they don't have good relations with their depart-

ment on the campus and we do. We need them, but they need us, too. They need us to help them with fourth year clinical students. They need us to supervise, to offer them training experiences with patients—in therapy and in diagnosis.

The two respondents immediately above imply that they not only need the power of the Department of Psychology so they will not be at the "mercy" of psychiatrists, but that in exchange for power they help the campus department in the training of graduate students.

In any case, the above comments reveal that psychologists perceive psychiatrists as possessing power and control over them, and it is only through their alignment with the campus department that they feel psychiatrists' power is restricted. The alignment can, then, be viewed as a coalition in which the power of psychiatry is abated (or at least the psychologists see it this way). We recall, however, that power may be of two types—facilities or rewards, and that previous data suggest that reactions to the other's power will vary depending on whether the other's power resides in facilities or rewards. In general, data have suggested that an actor cannot coerce another to adopt respectful, appreciative, and accepting attitudes toward him. But the above remarks show that psychologists see the campus department precisely in terms of its ability to exert coercion. Thus, when psychologists say they needed the campus department to apply *pressure* on the Department of Psychiatry to prevent the restriction of their psychotherapeutic activities, they imply that the psychiatrists' power is primarily in the realm of *facilities*. It appears that concern is not with psychiatrists' respecting, or refusing to respect, their ability to do psychotherapy, but only with psychiatrists' allowing them to do it (and to do it independently and autonomously—i.e., without close supervision). For example, one psychologist states: "There are some psychiatrists around here who think psychologists shouldn't do therapy. In terms of the attitude of psychiatrists toward psychology, I don't care as long as we do it." This is a very different statement from that of the "psychiatric" social worker who wants to perform casework treatment, but wants psychiatrists to accept her as a competent professional, *too*.

This is not to say that psychologists are unconcerned about psychiatrists' evaluation of them, as is indicated by the chief psychologist's comments regarding departmental restrictions on the psychologists' autonomy to do research and engage in private practice.

> The image of the psychologist is involved here. Clinical psychology is a new profession—less than fifty years old. Is he a clinical man, an applied man? Or is he a researcher and an academic man? Within psychology itself there is no clearly defined image. What we are doing here is we are striving to raise the professional status of the psychologist; to make him independent; to have the uniqueness of his activity recognized; to be recognized as an autonomous professional and not someone who is to service psychiatry and to be hired to perform a service function, to be what the psychiatrists call one of their ancillaries. The private practice of diagnostics by psychologists is discouraged here— so outside earnings are limited. *The way medicine here views psychologists is a problem*—they see us almost exclusively in terms of someone hired to perform a service function for them. In other medical settings this isn't always the case—the psychologist is more independent. . . . The prestige of the psychologist as a research person is higher in other places than it is here. We are doing some research and it is coming to be recognized. But there is this *old image—this image of a routine service person.*

The image psychiatrists have of psychology is, then, important; but its importance lies in the area of *facilities,* rather than that of rewards. The psychologist does not want psychiatrists to view psychologists as routine testers, not because it reflects a lack of respect for their competence, but because it restricts their autonomy—it prevents them from engaging in research and private practice. The psychiatrists' evaluation is not gratifying in and of itself (a reward), but is a means (facility) to an end. Their image of psychologists is important because, unlike in academic settings where psychologists are autonomous and independent, "in a medical setting, the medical man is in control." He controls the psychologist's autonomy and independence.

A parallel case is the social worker's desire not to be viewed as a welfare worker. The psychiatrist's image does not prevent her from performing her casework role, however; rather, it indicates that psychiatrists do not consider social workers as professionally competent and knowledgeable. To the social worker, a positive evaluation from psychiatry *is* a source of gratification that is an end in and of itself.

A more detailed examination of the expressed dissatisfaction of the restrictions on private practice provides additional material for further points of contrast between psychologists and social workers. In each case where dissatisfaction is expressed,[2] reference is also made to the fact that the restriction prevents psychologists from increasing their salary. It will be remembered that salary for social workers is an important expressive symbol, expressing the psychiatrists' degree of respect for them. In the case of the psychologists, the psychiatrists' significance, insofar as salaries are concerned, lies in their control over the means (facilities) to higher salaries. For example:

> We aren't allowed to do private practice here, but I think we should. I don't think it's right that we aren't allowed to do so. I think it's an injustice. Psychologists at _____ [nearby hospital] are hired like we are but are given more leeway—they are given the opportunity to do private practice. As a result, they make much more than we do.

Another states that restrictions on their right to do private practice "gripes a lot of us. Because of this, our income is substantially below [psychologists] in other parts of the country. We have no opportunities for consulting."

Two points deserve emphasis here. First, insofar as private practice and salary are prestige symbols, psychiatrists' control over the means to acquire them deprives psychologists of this much reward. But there is no evidence that psychologists interpret these restrictions as expressions of psychiatrists' lack of respect for their competence. Rather, psychiatrists are seen to impose the restrictions because they are "threatened" and "frightened at psychologists' doing psychotherapy and private practice." Certainly, to perceive psychiatrists as fearful of and threatened by them is not to see psychiatrists as being disrespectful of them. In any case, in contrast to the social workers, the significance of salary is not interpreted in terms of a lack of respect for psychologists' professional competence. Psychiatrists' significance appears to be purely instrumental: they control the means or facilities (the right to engage in private practice) to higher salaries.

The second and related point refers to the phenomena of evaluative and comparative reference groups. To social workers, salary symbolizes psychiatrists' evaluation of them, and they uti-

2. Four psychologists volunteer this complaint.

lize psychologists and nonprofessional personnel as comparative reference groups to determine what their rights are in reference to this symbol. Who the psychologists' evaluative reference groups are—groups from whom they receive prestige and expressive gratification—cannot be determined from the data.[3] However, and this is the important point, there is no reason to suspect that psychiatrists are a powerful source of evaluation. Indeed, there is evidence that psychiatrists, in the reference group context, are more important in terms of their *comparative* reference-group function. For example,

> private practice is reserved in this setting to the psychiatric staff. One third of their time is devoted to private practice and fees go into a private fund. In this way, however, they can augment their salaries up to 100%. This is important because someone with faculty status of around seven or eight thousand can double their salary. This makes for important differences between psychologists and psychiatrists. This means substantially that the higher psychologist makes less than the lowest psychiatrist— a senior psychologist makes less than a junior [staff] psychiatrist. This makes for intangible, but important, well, status differences.

Also, in contrast to the "psychiatric" social worker who feels that the social workers are not a unified group, and who prefers to remain a member of the Department of Psychiatry rather than be associated with a Department of Social Work, we have the following comments from psychologists.

> We see ourselves as a group; we are a group, not a member of a service like child or inpatient. It's funny but our allegiance is to the psychology department on the campus or to our [own] department here, not to the service we are on. Our allegiance is to psychology, not psychiatry. It's funny, we never think of ourselves as a member of a service, just the psychology department —here or on campus.

In commenting on the lack of independence and autonomy accorded the psychologists in the Department of Psychiatry, the supervisor states:

> In some places [other medical school settings] you have a behavioral science unit with a psychologist the head of his own department, where each head of a department communicates

3. For example, they may include the profession of psychology, the university community, or some vague generalized other such as "society."

with the dean. But here I have to communicate to him through _____ [Chairman of the Department of Psychiatry]. What the dean knows and hears he gets second hand from _____. I've never had an occasion to talk to the dean directly. Appeals here go through an additional channel which isn't true of an academic setting. I'm not saying the psychologists' views are inadequately represented, but they are not as adequately represented as if the psychologists had a spokesman.

This response again reveals psychiatrists' power over psychologists in the area of facilities: control over what is communicated to the Dean of the School of Medicine. The above two comments also reveal no desire to be associated with the Department of Psychiatry, as did the "psychiatric" social workers in their opposition to integration.

Although the above data are admittedly rather fragmentary, they all point in the same general direction: psychiatrists' importance to psychologists is in the realm of facilities rather than rewards. The psychiatrists' power rests on their ability to restrict the psychologists' autonomy and freedom to perform various instrumental roles, e.g., research and private practice. Psychiatrists also have such power over the social worker since they may restrict and hinder her performance of casework treatment, but they are a potent source of expressive gratification as well.

Still to be explained, however, are the psychologists' complaints that psychiatrists lack respect and appreciation for their diagnostic test data, complaints which are quite similar to those voiced by the "psychiatric" social workers. There is a major difference, however. The social workers' complaints are more diffuse and revolve around psychiatrists' failure to accord social workers respect in the performance of their primary role—casework treatment. The psychologists' complaints are more specific: they are voiced only in reference to their diagnostic role—their most generally disliked role. No psychologist complains that psychiatrists fail to respect the psychologist's competence and ability in research, psychotherapy, and teaching.

The question arises: why do psychologists voice these complaints about a role the majority do not especially like? It should be noted that those expressing a particular dislike for diagnosis —the research oriented—make these complaints as well as other psychologists: ten of eleven who perform this role express the complaint.[4] The five research oriented who are hired primarily for diagnostic work, plus one research oriented, volunteer that the MMPI and sentence completion tests are of limited value; but they also note that if their time must be devoted to this work, the work should receive greater appreciation. One states, for example,

> they [psychiatrists] don't think we are bringing up any insights with these tests that they can't get for themselves—which is probably true; but if we have to spend time doing the damn things, they should use them. A lot of them think these tests don't offer anything and would rather not be bothered by them. This would be fine with me; but if they want us to do this work, they should appreciate it a little more.

For the research oriented, this suggests that one factor involved in their complaints is their feeling that psychiatrists should appreciate their work, not because they need psychiatrists to confirm their belief that they perform important work, but because psychiatrists make them do the work. Also, psychiatrists' failure to listen to his report is probably insulting to any professional psychologist, not because he particularly wants respect from psychiatrists, but because it is insulting for others to ignore his opinion, no matter who the others are—psychiatrists or anybody else. Professional self-images are rarely insensitive to others' indifference.

Still, psychiatrists' expressive power to reward psychologists should not be underestimated. To the extent that psychologists attribute even a limited value to their tests, psychiatrists have the ability to reward them. Psychology, especially in the context of diagnosis, is still an "ancillary" profession—psychologists are in the Department primarily to provide a service for psychiatrists. Consequently, the psychologists' services, like those of any "ancillary" group, can be considered of value only if the physician uses these services in his treatment of patients. As a result, psychologists must necessarily depend on psychiatrists for a certain amount of reward. It may be true that psychiatrists do not have the same degree of expressive power over psychologists that they have over the social workers, but psychologists are rewarded when their service is used by psychiatrists. They "like to see

4. See p. 153, n. 4 above.

some effect from [their] work on other persons, to know that the [psychiatrists] are dependent on it," and they like to get "feedback"—to be told by the patient's therapist that their tests are helpful.[5]

There is one other factor involved in these complaints, perhaps the most important of all. Professional people are proud people. They are sensitive to the deference and respect of others. Indeed, their self-images depend on this. But when highly skilled persons from different professions work together in face-to-face relationships, it is probably inevitable that each will sometimes offend the other by failing to pay him proper respect and deference. Consequently, an important factor involved in these complaints about the psychiatrists' attitude toward diagnostic testing may stem from the inevitabilities of face-to-face contact between highly skilled professional groups. This is suggested by the remarks of a psychologist who performs no diagnostic work at all.

> Interviewer: Your responses indicate that you are something of an exception among psychologists. At least some of them indicate a concern with psychiatrists' attitude toward them. You don't indicate this at all.
>
> Psychologist: No, I have very little difficulty there as I have very little contact with psychiatrists, actually. I don't do any diagnostics, so I don't work with them much.
>
> Interviewer: You seem to be sort of, I want to use the term, sheltered from psychiatrists, but that isn't quite the right word [interrupted].
>
> Psychologist: Yes, that's right. I have very little dealings with them. It's not like diagnostics: if I can't get along with them, I don't fool with them. I do what I want to do.

Since he has little contact with psychiatrists, psychiatrists are unable to jeopardize his self-image.

SUMMARY AND CONCLUSIONS

This chapter has suggested that the primary significance psychiatrists have for psychologists in the context of power is in the realm of instrumental facilities. Data indicate that a major difference between the clinical psychologists and social workers—

5. See p. 150 above.

particularly the "psychiatric" social workers—lies in the fact that psychiatrists are an important source of rewards as well as facilities. Although psychologists express complaints similar to those of the social workers, it appears not to be due to psychiatrists' being a major evaluative reference group for them.

PART IV

CONCLUSIONS AND IMPLICATIONS

13 CONCLUSIONS AND IMPLICATIONS

We have described the actions of four professional groups in a mental hospital and made several theoretical generalizations. In this concluding chapter we will bring together the salient findings and conclusions under the following headings: power strategies and the institutional and noninstitutional, the function of normative rules, instrumental and expressive orientations, and reference groups. Central to our concern will be the relevance of our findings to an understanding of the institutionalization process. And although this is not a study of complex social organization (bureaucracy), certain of its implications for an understanding of social processes within complex organizations will be outlined. Finally, practical implications for modern mental hospital social organization will be suggested.

POWER STRATEGIES AND THE INSTITUTIONAL AND NONINSTITUTIONAL

Power strategies are sociologically relevant types of behavior since they are directed to the behavior of others. Still they do not conform to the general category of institutionalized behavior. At the same time, they can be understood only when considered in terms of the institutionalized orders within which they are enacted, for they are oriented to the legitimate—institutionalized— order. The nurses' deference behavior, for example, was oriented to the authority (legitimate order) of the doctor: nurses thought

237

they knew more than the doctor, but were "careful" not to act as if they did. Yet to consider this behavior as merely oriented to a legitimate order ignores one of its important properties— the attempt to influence. The noninstitutional power strategy has elements of the institutional in it, but it is inadequately explained in terms of institutionalized rules of conduct alone.

The relationship of power strategies to the institutionalized order is further clarified by the typology of power strategies: implementing cost-inducing, structural cost-reducing, and maintaining cost-preventing power strategies.[1] We hypothesized that this typology is related to the institutionalization process: the character of the particular power strategy—its function for the actor—depends upon the degree to which social relationships have been institutionalized.

Implementing strategies are characteristic of situations in which the actor-other relationship is minimally institutionalized. Indeed, many of the recreator's attempts to become an institutionalized feature of the Department were classified as implementing strategies. The implementation of the recreation program entailed her dependence upon residents, patients, and nurses. But she was new to the Department and had few institutionalized relationships with these personnel. She consequently had difficulty getting them to respond in accordance with the needs of her program. In addition, she felt that others failed to realize a Department recreation service existed. For these reasons she had to work fifty-five to sixty hours per week to implement her program.

The residents' failure to send her referrals was met with various power strategies: attending ward rounds and team meetings, asking questions, *tertius gaudens,* introducing herself, and being seen. These strategies required her physical presence and were costly—e.g., they were time consuming. She attempted to eliminate these costly activities by introducing a referral form. If this had been accepted, it would have put the recreator-resident relationship on a permanent (institutionalized) basis, insofar as referrals were concerned. This was a structural strategy.

1. As we have seen, the problem of influencing the other's use of rewards poses problems for the actor which are not encountered when the attempt is solely to influence the other's use of facilities. The typology of power strategies refers to the actor's attempts to influence the other's use of facilities only.

These findings led to the hypothesis that the two strategies correspond to two separate stages of the institutionalization process: (1) A stage in which power strategies must be used, but must also be kept up because the other is not yet obligated to act consistently with the actor's wishes. Because they must be continually exerted, they are cost-inducing. (2) The introduction of a formal rule which, if accepted by the other party, puts the relationship on an established (institutionalized) basis and eliminates the need for strategies utilized in the first stage. Successful strategies of the second stage—structural strategies—are therefore cost-reducing: the other's acceptance of the rule eliminates the need to influence his compliance.

The recreator's influencing ("motivating") patients to respond to "their" recreation program was interpreted in similar terms. She attempted to eliminate costly implementing strategies by introducing a structural strategy, namely, getting nursing personnel to perform the costly implementing activities for her.

Social workers had worked in the Department for a number of years and, therefore, did not experience some of the problems encountered by the recreator, such as others not knowing of their existence nor having to work additional hours to elicit others' compliance. Yet, there was no formal definition of the social workers' role in the Department; and although social workers defined their role as casework treatment, this was not wholly congruent with the psychiatrists' conception of their role. Also, like the recreator, they were dependent upon residents for important facilities—case referral and collaborative information —to perform their role. They too experienced the problem of residents not co-operating.

To influence the residents' referral of cases the social workers had to employ implementing strategies: "tact," *tertius gaudens,* etc. These actions involved the cost of "extra effort"—e.g., having to "chase the resident down," as well as the costs of awkwardness, discomfort, and generally having to do things they felt they should not have to do. Consistent with the recreator, social workers responded with structural strategies: attempts to evoke a norm and establish a coalition with staff psychiatrists.

The analyses of the recreator and social workers indicate that rules which regulate and control (institutionalize) the activity of others may be viewed in terms of two simultaneous processes: cost-inducing processes and cost-reducing processes. Accordingly, institutions give rise to cost-reducing processes by structuring *out* cost-inducing activities. Both the recreator and social workers introduced such rules in an attempt to reduce the costs imposed by unco-operative others.

The recreator was new to the service and therefore had few institutionalized relationships with significant others. Because of this, and because the study was a brief longitudinal one, the historical sequence of the hypothesized two-step process of institutionalization was clearly seen. This was especially true for her relationship with the residents. The same processes were present in the case of the social workers, although they were seen more in terms of their co-existence than as separate aspects of a historical process.

According to this formulation, *if* the recreator and social workers had been successful in their structural strategies, the new structures would have reduced cost-inducing activities. The validity of this interpretation is suggested by interview responses from the recreator and social workers, and from the analysis of a structural change in the inpatient service admissions procedure which affected the social worker-resident relationship.[2]

The power strategy concept was useful in the analysis of the recreator and social workers for describing actions which occur under conditions of limited institutionalization—as is the case with implementing strategies—and actions designed to create institutionalization—such as structural strategies. Power strategies are also exhibited under more institutionalized conditions, however. Indeed, the nurses' deference toward the doctor is clearly compounded with aspects of a traditional, institutionalized nurse-doctor relationship. In fact, her deferential influence attempts are noninstitutionalized influence attempts which are generated by a conflict in the institutional order—conflict between normative principles of the nurse role: patient welfare and the obligation to carry out the doctor's order. Most nurses tried to solve this conflict by according the doctor deference in an attempt to effect a change in his order which was more consistent with their conception of the patient's welfare. Because the power strategies were deferential in nature, they were oriented to the normative order that the doctor is the nurse's superior. But to be

2. Analysis of the psychologists also supports the general hypothesis that institutionalized rules function to reduce costs. See the following section.

oriented to the normative order is not to say that they were pre-scribed by it, that is, that they were institutionalized.

Such actions maintain the relational system and prevent costs. The nurse was very much dependent upon a face-to-face rela-tionship with the resident through which the resident gave her instructions in how she should relate to particular patients. The nurse realized that the expression of her true opinion would alienate the resident—e.g., the relationship with the resident would be "ruined," or it would "blow-up." Such "blow-ups" would deprive the nurse of needed facilities (directives and guidance), thereby placing her in a costly situation (e.g., a "bad position" or an "insecure" position). This would be costly be-cause she must then relate to patients without knowing what she should do—e.g., what she should talk about; as a consequence, she would forgo the value of the resident's directives. To retain this value—that is, to maintain her relationship with the resi-dent—she utilized deference to influence him, rather than telling him what she really thinks. Such strategies *prevent* costs.

We argued that because they function to maintain the rela-tional system, cost-preventing strategies characterize social re-lationships which have attained a high degree of institutional-ization. The formulation is, therefore, that implementing strate-gies predominate under conditions of minimum institutionaliza-tion; structural strategies—particularly rules and norms—are then introduced to cut costs and stabilize and institutionalize the relationship; but once the relationship has been institutionalized, strategies may take on the character of maintaining cost-pre-venting functions for the actor.

It would appear that the nature of social interaction is such that few relationships are so completely institutionalized that re-ciprocal influence among participants is completely controlled and regulated by institutionalized rules of conduct. Accordingly, a concept like power strategy which refers to noninstitutionalized influence attempts would appear to be needed for more complete analyses of most social relationships. This might be particularly true in the case of superordinate-subordinate relationships. There may be an inherent instability in such relationships that social norms never completely eliminate.[3] If so, concepts are needed to

3. The following works support this thesis: Ralf Dahrendorf, *Class and Class Conflict in Industrial Society* (Palo Alto: Stanford University Press, 1959), pp. 157-79; and George C. Homans, *Social Behavior: Its Elementary Forms* (New York: Harcourt, Brace, and World, Inc., 1961), pp. 283-315.

describe actions stemming from such strain and tension, as well as the functions performed by these actions in resolving the strain and tension. A concept like power strategy does this.

Regarding the classification of power strategies, we should re-emphasize the point that distinctions between power strategies are analytic distinctions. Any concrete strategy may be cost inducing under some circumstances and cost preventing under other circumstances. For example, *tertius gaudens* was a cost-inducing strategy in the case of the recreator, but a cost-preventing one for the nurses. Also, the same strategy may have different functions for the same actor. If the nurse has strong needs for prestige and demonstration of her competence and knowledge, failure to express her true opinion to the resident may be cost inducing. To the extent that she values her relationship with the resident, however, she must forgo these other values.

The social workers' strategies may also be interpreted as performing two different functions: cost inducing and cost preventing. Social workers often thought they were better informed than residents about the need for social service on particular cases, but they did not convey this opinion to the residents. Instead, they used strategies such as "tact" to influence them. For them not to have shown outward respect for the residents' superior competence might have resulted in their doing less casework treatment since the residents had the power to prevent them from so doing. They, too, had to respect status differences between themselves and residents. (For example, one social worker reported that the resident took her off the case when she failed to observe these status differences—e.g., she allegedly was doing a better job treating the relative than he was in treating the patient.) Furthermore, there may be a complex interweaving of different strategies in the actions of the same actor. For instance, the recreator employed the structural strategy of getting nursing personnel established into "gaps" (performing costly activities that the recreator was having to perform). She attempted to do this through the strategy of "interpersonal relationships." These, too, were time consuming. She thus attempted to replace cost-inducing activity with a cost-reducing strategy, the establishment of which required cost-inducing (time-consuming) strategies.

Finally, the power strategy typology might provide a useful conceptual scheme for the classification of organizations. Organizations that comprise social relationships which are based predominantly on strong tradition—such as the doctor-nurse relationship—may be characterized primarily by the existence of maintaining strategies. There may be occasions in which power strategies are necessary, but organizational participants are "careful" not to disrupt the traditionally based status structure. In newly born organizations, such as modern therapeutically oriented mental hospitals, agreed-upon mutual role obligations between professional groups may not have developed. Relationships between professions may be characterized greatly by implementing power strategies, as well as by institutionalized role behavior. Still other organizations may be in the stage in which rules (structural strategies) are beginning to crystallize. These considerations reveal that in addition to the power strategy scheme's potential for distinguishing cycles of an organization's development and change, it could also be used for the comparative analysis of organizations.

THE FUNCTION OF INSTITUTIONALIZED RULES

The analysis of the psychologist's diagnostic role supports the hypothesis implied in the conception of structural power strategy: institutions (rules), when applied to the other upon whom the actor is dependent, reduce the actor's costs. Contrary to the referral procedure for recreation and social service, referral for psychological testing was not subject to the individual judgment of the resident, nor did it require face-to-face contact between psychologists and residents. Because residents' decision to refer patients for psychological testing was a matter of organizational SOP and routine, rather than a function of individual judgment regarding the needs of patients, psychologists experienced a minimum of costs performing their diagnostic role.

The view that rules are cost reducing does not deny that they may have cost-inducing features also. The routine referral procedure for psychological tests was cost reducing for psychologists—it controlled the residents' behavior; but it also restricted the residents' autonomy to prescribe services for their patients. If greater autonomy for residents is desired, this institutionalized procedure is cost inducing, for residents must forgo a value—their autonomy. The bureaucratization of diagnostic testing also had a cost-inducing aspect for psychologists. In Chapter 6 we saw that too much routine diagnostic work was structured into their work schedule to allow them the desired autonomy and freedom to conduct research. For at least one psychologist, it also placed too many restraints on his freedom to teach. This problem was greatly reduced for other psychologists because of joint academic appointments in the Department of Psychology and Department of Psychiatry.

Thus, while our hypothesis is that rules function to reduce costs for someone, the hypothesis must always be specified: cost reducing for whom and in reference to what. For different actors, and for the same actor in different contexts, the same cost-reducing rule may be cost inducing. This does not invalidate the fundamental cost-reducing hypothesis, however.

We have spoken of organizational rules in terms of their value and cost to individual actors. When the above hypothesis is applied to the organization as a whole, it implies that bureaucratic rules and routine contribute to organizational effectiveness. To some degree this is true. An organization cannot attain maximum effectiveness if large numbers of its members incur excessive costs of time and energy through the exertion of influence attempts. Organizational rules often persist, however, even though they have little or no functional value for the organization's purposive goals. Muzafer Sherif expresses the point this way: "In the initial state, norms may express the actual relationships demanded by the situation and may serve to regulate the lives of the individual members in a group along co-operative lines with little friction. But, once formed, they tend to persist. Many times they outlive their usefulness." [4] In certain instances, they may be in conflict with the goals of the organization.

The analysis contained in this study suggests why norms may persist in the face of their uselessness (to the organization). As many who are familiar with large-scale organizations know, rules, once formed, do tend to persist. But they do not *just* persist, as Sherif implies. For someone, they serve a purpose: ". . . institutions do not keep going because they are enshrined in norms. . . . They keep going because they have pay-offs, ultimately pay-offs for individuals." [5] And important among their pay-offs is cost-reduction: institutions control behavior, thereby eliminating the necessity for the costs of surveillance and power

4. Muzafer Sherif, *The Psychology of Social Norms* (New York: Harper, 1936), p. 198.
5. Homans, *Social Behavior: Its Elementary Forms*, p. 390.

strategies to assure compliance. Consequently, members may oppose changes in organizational rules because they fear that such changes will place them in situations requiring the use of costly power strategies to elicit compliance. Thus, organizational members may come to have a vested interest in the maintenance of the structure because of their desire to cut costs, as well as their desire to implement the organization's purposive goals.

The study of the recreator provides us with an illustration of the conflict between the individual's desire—indeed, need—for routine and the goals of the organization. The emphasis on "individuation"—the adjustment of nursing activities to the constantly changing therapeutic needs of patients—created costs for the recreator. The standardization or routinization of the nurses' activities would have contributed much to a reduction of these costs. However, this undoubtedly would have had negative consequences for the organizational goal of patient care. Here, the need for the individual actor (recreator) to reduce costs and the requirements of the organization were clearly in conflict.

Two other illustrations imply the same conclusion. The routine referral procedure for psychological tests cuts costs for the psychologist. The same procedure reduces the residents' autonomy. One may argue that one of the essentials of medical education is to teach the prospective physician to operate autonomously. To be deprived of autonomy in referrals for psychological tests may, then, deprive the resident of valuable educational experience. Also, a routine referral procedure for social service may have reduced the social workers' need for costly implementing strategies at the expense of the residents' autonomy to prescribe services for their patients.

Finally, the above considerations cast light on the complex problem of social power in social organizations. Ultimately, social power refers to the acts of men. In our specific usage it refers to the handling of facilities and rewards upon which others are dependent. Failure to utilize these "possessions" in the interests of others is cost inducing for others. But as we have shown, costs may be structured out by the establishment of social rules. It follows, then, that one's power is very much a function of the degree to which his behavior is controlled and regulated by social rules. Rules which structure out one's ability to induce costs also structure out one's power. Therefore, organizational power structures, which exist in the interrelated acts of organizational members, can be studied in terms of the extent to which they are contained and controlled by rules and norms. Organizations could be compared in terms of their normative control of the power structure. Research could aim to determine the optimal balance between the normative structure and the power structure for organizational effectiveness. Some organizations may require a highly controlled—bureaucratized—power structure; others may require a less rigidly controlled power structure.

INSTRUMENTAL AND EXPRESSIVE ORIENTATIONS

In Chapter 2 we raised the question of whether the actor's problem of obtaining rewards from others is essentially a different problem from his obtaining facilities. Studies of the recreator, social workers, and psychologists cast light on this question.

On several occasions we suggested that the attempt to influence the other to comply with facilities would have also obtained rewards. The recreator's attempts to get referrals from residents were attempts to get recognition from them as well. We also inferred that, had the referral form been accepted, it would have served as an expressive symbol. The social workers' attempt to create an administrative committee was perceived by them in terms of its expressive functions. It would have supplemented (or replaced) the supervisor in the social workers' quest for higher salaries and faculty status, as well as reflecting psychiatrists' concern for their contribution. Their attempt to evoke a norm defining their role as one of casework treatment would have been an appreciative standard symbolizing psychiatrists' professional respect for them. And finally, although the structural change in the inpatient admissions procedure was not itself a strategy, it was compounded with both instrumental and expressive properties. It not only facilitated the social workers' performance of casework treatment, but for one social worker it symbolized psychiatrists' professional acceptance of social workers.

The above illustrations reveal the fusion of instrumental and expressive orientations in the same structure and influence attempt. On the other hand, other illustrations reveal conflict between the two.

First, the recreator's use of *tertius gaudens,* which she used to force ("motivate") the residents to send her referrals, could not get her rewards. For residents to reward her—to express a value for her services—they had to use her services voluntarily. Consequently, *tertius gaudens* could get her facilities (referrals), but it could not get her rewards.

Another example is the proposed structural change which would have assigned social workers to individual psychiatrists. Because it would have given the individual social worker a closer relationship with the staff psychiatrist, it was perceived by some as a means of better controlling the resident's use of facilities. Yet, it was collectively opposed on expressive grounds. Social workers wanted to be "seen" as a group and as a separate profession.

Additional data revealed not only that the actor sometimes fails to get the others' rewards when he gets facilities, but that the problem of obtaining rewards is more complex and difficult. This stems from the fact that the other's reward is an *attitude* of appreciation, respect, acceptance and regard. For the recreator, this attitude was expressed by the psychiatrists' voluntary act. Their use of her service, without her urging, symbolized their respect. As we pointed out above, she could coerce residents to send her referrals, but she could not coerce their voluntary response.

Social workers, more than any other group, experienced the problem of significant others (psychiatrists) withholding rewards. The problem was expressed in a variety of ways: demands for higher salaries and faculty status, not being seen as a group, being seen as a welfare worker, etc. The underlying theme in all of these expressed dissatisfactions was the lack of (perceived) respect from psychiatrists. Thus, the social workers' problem was to correct the psychiatrists' attitude toward them. Rather than approaching the problem directly, however, they "acted out" and made demands for faculty status and higher salaries; they tried to make psychiatrists accord them certain publicly recognized symbols of professional respect. As the supervisors implied, however, you cannot make the other respect you; you must demonstrate your competence to him *first*. "If you make a contribution, it will be recognized and appreciated." The problem of obtaining rewards is, then, a problem of achievement rather than ascription. In the same connection, a psychiatrist told the social workers they would be accepted when they proved they were "worthy" and could make a contribution.

Concerning the relative differences between the institutionalization of the other's facilities on the one hand and his rewards on the other, the above illustrations imply that rules can be imposed to elicit facilities, but they may be ineffective for obtaining expressive responses. Support for this thesis was found in the study of the psychologists' diagnostic role. Organizational rules had routinized and institutionalized the psychiatrists' use of facilities (i.e., referrals), so that the psychologists experienced little difficulty eliciting co-operative instrumental responses. However, the psychologists' reports that psychiatrists sometimes failed to express appreciation and respect for their testing reports indicate that psychiatrists' expressive responses had not been so institutionalized.

Data from all three services, then, point to the conclusion that the other's evaluative attitudes of respect and appreciation, acceptance and regard, cannot be coerced. Even if his use of facilities is controlled (institutionalized), he still may not convey the attitudes that are a source of the actor's expressive gratification. The institutionalization of the expressive structure is a problem which must be solved *in addition to* the institutionalization of the instrumental structure.

These findings provide additional implications for complex organizations, particularly regarding the problem of participant motivation. The recreator, social workers, and psychologists clearly indicated that they not only wanted facilities from others; they also wanted rewards. Robert Dubin points out that the organizational source for motivating organizational personnel is the prestige structure.[6] And as we have indicated—particularly in the study of the social workers—prestige is basically a problem of evaluative attitudes. Consequently, the motivation of organizational participants is dependent upon significant others' expressing an attitude of respect for them. Accordingly, the institutionalization of the organizational affective structure may be an important component of organizational effectiveness.

Since the institutionalization of rewards does not *necessarily* accompany the institutionalization of facilities, rules may elicit co-operation from organizational members, but they may not result in expressions of respect and appreciation. Consequently, the organization may solve the problem of institutionalizing the structure of facilities without simultaneously solving problems

6. Robert Dubin, *The World of Work* (Englewood Cliffs, N. J.: Prentice-Hall, Inc., 1958), p. 55.

of the affective structure of rewards. Since the latter is related to motivation, participants of the organization may not be sufficiently motivated. Alvin Gouldner makes the point this way:

> What we mean by "bureaucratization" is, in part, the explication of the group member's rights and obligations through the installation of formal rules and obligations. In other words, the more an organization is bureaucratized (and this is clearly a variable), the more the conforming behavior of people in the organization will tend to be perceived as imposed on them by rules, rather than as voluntary. . . . Consequently, the more conforming actions will be devalued in that they will yield smaller increments of appreciation or gratitude which can motivate reciprocity. . . .[7]

In other words, if the other's response becomes too routinized, the reward power of his response is reduced. His response becomes a function of formal rules, rather than the result of his attitudes concerning the value of the actor's work.[8]

Indeed, this phenomenon appeared in the routine procedure of diagnostic testing referrals. Psychologists experienced no problem co-ordinating their activities with those of the psychiatrists, but they did feel that psychiatrists expressed a lack of respect for their testing reports. The use of psychological tests had become a matter of routine, rather than a voluntary decision expressing the psychiatrists' need, and therefore value, for the psychologists' work. That this involves a problem of motivation was illustrated by the psychologist who gave "garbage reports" to psychiatrists who fail to appreciate his work.

Here we see where an organization may be caught in a dilemma between the institutionalization of the structure of facilities and the institutionalization of the affective structure of rewards. We have stated that, up to a point at least, organizational effectiveness is increased when activities are co-ordinated by a set of organizational rules. However, the implication of the above illustration is that an increase in the institutionalization of the

7. Alvin W. Gouldner, "Organizational Analysis," in Robert K. Merton, Leonard Broom, and Leonard S. Cottrell, Jr. (eds.), *Sociology Today* (New York: Basic Books, 1959), pp. 425-26.
8. George Simmel's comments on the salute as a symbol of respect is relevant here. "The salute upon the street by no means demonstrates respect; . . . As symbols of positive subjective attitude, the forms completely fail to be of service." "The Number of Members as Determining the Sociological Form of the Group," trans. Albion W. Small, *American Journal of Sociology*, VI (1902), 17.

instrumental structure may result in a certain measure of expressive deprivation.

Thus, an actor may impose a rule on another's activity in an effort to get his co-operation in the use of facilities. As a result, he may come to experience a problem of expressive deprivation: the other may co-operate with him as a matter of routine, and not because he respects him or his work. Also, administrators may impose formal rules and regulations in an effort to co-ordinate activities in the interest of organizational goals; co-ordination of facilities may be achieved, but with a consequent reduction in the motivation to produce. Co-operation and interaction may be expressed in terms of formal routine and not in terms of the attitudes of appreciation and respect.

This raises the question of the optimal condition for motivating organizational members. In the case of the recreator, we saw that part of her reason for working so many hours was to secure recognition. Others' failure to provide her with gratifying rewards motivated her to work harder (or at least longer) in an effort to get these rewards. This suggests that the affective structure should not be maximally institutionalized. The organizational participant should experience a certain uncertainty about others' rewarding him. If the actor is satisfied that he will receive the rewarding attitudes of others, he has no problem. If he is uncertain, however, he is more likely to try to influence others' attitudes toward him.[9] He cannot do this by imposing rules on them, or by trying to "make" them respect his work. But he may by demonstrating his competence through hard work. The psychologists, for example, indicated that there was nothing they could do, other than to demonstrate their competence and do their "best," when psychiatrists failed to show respect for their reports.

Although this implies that the affective structure should be short of maximal institutionalization, other data indicate that

9. As noted above, the classification of power strategies is limited to attempts to influence others' use of facilities. We have found that the problem of influencing others' use of rewards is more complex and difficult, and that one's reactions to others who withhold rewards tend to be different from his reactions to others who withhold facilities. However, other than recognizing that performing one's work more competently may be an attempt to influence others' attitudes, we have no data showing how actors attempt to influence others' evaluative attitudes. Further research could attempt to ascertain methods of such influence attempts, and to determine if different strategies are related to different stages of institutionalization.

participants should not be too deprived of others' expressive responses. Under these conditions the participant may cease to be motivated, as was the case of the psychologist who gave "garbage reports." Under more serious depriving conditions, such as in the case of the social workers, participants may proceed to "act out" and demand greater prestige, which may center on symbols. The basic problem may be lost sight of, for participants see the problem in terms of symbols, rather than deficient expressive institutionalization; and work time is spent discussing dissatisfaction without solving the problem. Such seems to have been the fate of the committee established to study the dissatisfactions of the social workers. The organization may come to lose competent personnel.

Recognition of both expressive and instrumental dimensions of organizational structures may reveal points and sources of conflict in complex organizations. In some cases the conflicting demands may not be resolvable. The social workers provide an illustration. They were expressively deprived because they felt psychiatrists did not give them the proper professional respect. One way in which they perceived this lack of respect was in reference to the educational structure: psychiatric trainees were permitted to perform casework treatment. Consequently, social workers' achievement of expressive gratification would have entailed, for one thing, excluding residents from performing casework treatment. Otherwise, the *uniqueness* of social work skills and competence would go unrecognized. But this would have led to less emphasis on resident education, one of the organization's major instrumental objectives. Thus, to institutionalize certain expressive aspects of the organization would have conflicted with paramount organizational goals.

We suggested above that participants may resist changes in organizational rules and routine because of their need to maintain the structure and cut costs. The basic argument there was that the change may function to deprive the actor of necessary facilities. Changes may also be resisted because they deprive the actor of rewards. The structural change integrating medical and psychiatric social work provides us with such an illustration. The change had no instrumental disadvantage, but it was opposed because of its symbolic meaning and consequent expressive deprivation. Psychiatric social workers did not want to be integrated with medical social workers because the medical profession failed to accord medical social workers as much professional respect and recognition as they did psychiatric social workers.

REFERENCE GROUPS

The reference group scheme was applied to the recreator and to the psychologists, but its primary utility was found in the analysis of the social workers' problem of expressive deprivation. The importance of psychiatrists as an evaluative reference group varied with the way social workers defined their role. Those who emphasized a casework role were also the ones who indicated the strongest desire to be respected by psychiatrists. The differences in role definition were interpreted as a function of differences in normative reference groups. This suggests the usefulness of reference group concepts for revealing the relationship between an actor's instrumental and expressive orientations.

The use of the concept of evaluative reference group, and its distinction from a comparative reference group, appear to be particularly necessary. It refers to those groups from whom an actor especially wants expressive responses. He utilizes comparative reference groups to ascertain the extent to which he receives desired rewards (i.e., prestige) from the evaluative reference group. Organizational prestige structures can then be analyzed in terms of these two concepts. It is through evaluative reference groups that prestige is bestowed. One's prestige is not a mere function of the absolute rewards he gets, but is also a function of how much reward other groups receive. For example, one way in which the social workers determined how they were evaluated by psychiatrists was to compare the way they were "treated" by psychiatrists with the way psychiatrists treated psychologists and nonprofessional personnel. Therefore, their deprivation was, largely, relative deprivation. This reveals that, from the individual actor's point of view, the organizational prestige hierarchy may be viewed as a series of comparative reference groups. One compares himself with others below him and above him to determine how much prestige he has.

These concepts, along with the recognition that various symbols are reflections of prestige, provide a scheme for explaining a recurring problem in complex organizations. Administrators' efforts to satisfy the expressive demands of one group by according them additional privileges may be met with similar demands from other groups. This is understandable because privileges are an important aspect of the prestige structure, and because the prestige of one group is a relative function of the prestige of other groups.

Regarding normative reference groups, the analysis of the social workers reveals the organization's lack of control over the way members may define their role within the organization. Only the social worker who indicated a lack of identification with the social work profession chose to define her role primarily in terms of organizational considerations. The others defined their role in reference to the standards of the profession of social work. Within this group, as we indicated above, those emphasizing a casework treatment role were also the ones who were oriented to psychiatrists as an evaluative reference group.

SOME PRACTICAL IMPLICATIONS

The reader will have recognized that our emphasis has been predominantly sociological and academic, rather than practical. Effort has been made to preserve a theoretical continuity throughout; we have attempted to formulate each research problem and make conclusions in the most general theoretical terms. It would be unfortunate, however, if we had nothing to say regarding the practical aspects of hospital organization and administration.

Often, books uncovering organizational conflicts and tensions close with recommendations which would eliminate them. We have no such panaceas. It is our opinion that many organizational problems described in this book are not solvable within the present structure and organization of mental hospitals and mental health professions, and many attempts to solve them may be accompanied by serious negative consequences. Nevertheless, an awareness of these problems and their sources may permit more intelligent decisions by hospital personnel. Accordingly, we will outline what seem to us to be the major factors producing these problems and various consequences of alternative courses of action. Awareness of the source of problems and the possible consequences of attempts to correct them may prevent hasty and disruptive administrative action.

At the outset we should note that many tensions may be resolved without necessitating special administrative action. There may be built-in corrective mechanisms, such as the nurses' deference behavior, which resolve organizational conflict before it has serious disruptive results. In such cases, administrators may be unaware that the problem and its potentially disruptive consequences exist.

In the first chapter we stated that an underlying source of tension among mental hospital personnel was the ambiguous and conflicting role definitions among mental health professions, because in great part of the relative youth of these professions. This was most clearly illustrated in the case of the recreation service, for which the residents, patients, and nursing personnel appeared to have no image consistent with the recreator's. For a new profession to establish a well-defined role requires time; for several new professions with overlapping skills to agree on their respective roles takes even longer. As the authors of one study state regarding the role relationship between psychiatrists and clinical psychologists: "What the eventual distinction between the functions of the two groups may turn out to be . . . is undecided, and doubtless will not be worked through for some time." [10] This, of course, reflects our thesis that a modern mental hospital is in the process of institutionalization. Local hospital administrators are, therefore, helpless to eliminate a source of conflicting role conceptions involving a social process of national scope. They may expect organizational problems having their origin in this process to continue.

Involved also may be a conflict between organizational requirements and professionalization. Professional persons, whose primary criteria for defining their role are their professional standards, may be too rigid and inflexible to adjust to local hospital needs. For example, most social workers had difficulty adjusting their role to the educational needs of a teaching hospital; and psychologists, while realizing that their primary role was routine testing, nevertheless aspired to the more academic roles of research and teaching. Mental hospitals thus face a problem common to many complex organizations in modern society. Members of different professions enter the organization with preconceived pictures of their role and how organizational services should be provided. When organizational practices are incongruent with these pictures, conflict results. Conflict between organizational demands and professional demands regarding one's

10. Alvin Zander, Arthur R. Cohen, and Ezra Stotland, *Role Relations in the Mental Health Professions* (Ann Arbor: Institute for Social Research, 1957), p. 62.

proper function, while not unique to mental hospitals, is probably more acute in mental hospitals than most organizations because of the presence of many different professional groups with different backgrounds.

More than that, the modern therapeutic mental hospital, unlike its custodially oriented predecessor, is often a center for education and research, as well as treatment. Consequently, "ancillaries" such as social workers, who are oriented primarily to treatment, may be faced with a decision: either leave the organization—as four in our study did—or accept the educational and research emphasis and what this implies for their role within the organization—as the "local" did. On the other hand, the administrator has a choice—indeed, he is responsible for making this choice: either inform the group in question of the organization's aims and its consequence for the group's function within the organization, or modify the organization to make it congruent with what the group considers to be its proper function. It is true that should the first alternative be selected, the organization may lose competent "ancillaries"; but those who remain will at least know where they stand and will likely be less dissatisfied accordingly.

There are other instances where administrative action may have more clear-cut positive results. Administrative decrees which required that inpatient social workers interview relatives upon patient admission appeared to have clarified the inpatient social worker's role. Similar action from administrative psychiatrists' clarifying the recreator's role to resident and nursing personnel may have had similar results for the recreator. The argument that bureaucratic rules and regulations frustrate the actions of "ancillary" personnel [11] is only half true. Sometimes this may be the case, but as we saw in the case of the clinical psychologist's diagnostic role, as well as in the above mentioned instance of inpatient social workers, it is not always so. Depending upon the circumstances, rules and regulations may permit, rather than prevent, professional autonomy. The problem for the administrator is, therefore, to discover those areas where rules may be applied to the advantage of the "ancillary" without, at the same time, imposing undue restrictions on the actions of others. The psycholo-

---

11. See Milton Greenblatt, Richard H. York, and Ester Lucile Brown, *From Custodial to Therapeutic Patient Care in Mental Hospitals* (New York: Russell Sage Foundation, 1955), pp. 421-22.

gists' desire for more autonomy and independence reveals the restrictions and dissatisfaction that bureaucratic routine may generate.

The above problems reflect the general problem of role differentiation and co-ordination. Different roles should make a positive contribution to patient welfare without duplicating each other's functions. At the same time, roles should be co-ordinated so that the activities of different members do not conflict. The fact that these problems may be difficult to resolve is evidenced by the lack of role differentiation between social workers and residents, insofar as in-take and casework services were concerned. Even when role differentiation presents no severe problem—such as between the role of recreator and resident—co-ordination of activities may remain problematical. Description of the psychologist's diagnosis role is evidence that the problems of differentiation and co-ordination may be solved, however. The administration of psychological tests is clearly different from activities of other groups, yet the activity is co-ordinated with that of the group with whom the psychologist most closely works—psychiatrists. In general, role clarity and agreement facilitate the solution of the dual problems of differentiation and co-ordination.

At other times it may be best to leave roles unclearly defined, however. From the viewpoint of some psychiatrists, the social workers' function was "welfare," not casework. Formalization of this definition would have undoubtedly resulted in greater dissatisfaction among social workers. It would have also led to severe problems in recruiting social workers. The organization may have been left with less competent social workers.

In this connection we will offer a suggestion which may seem quite fey to some. It is part of the American value and belief system that one should hire the best man available for a particular job. Yet if it is true that psychiatrists primarily want only a routine-testing function from clinical psychologists and a welfare function from social workers, this may not be the best policy. The more competent social workers and psychologists are likely to find little satisfaction performing these roles, whereas less competent persons may perform them adequately and be satisfied, too. From an organizational viewpoint, it may sometimes be better to hire the average and mediocre rather than the best. In any case, unanticipated negative consequences are likely to accompany the policy of "hiring the best." The most competent professionals are not always the easiest persons to administrate.

If the hospital's reputation depends on the competence of "ancillaries" as well as the competence of psychiatrists, however, the administrator may face a dilemma: either hire less competent "ancillaries" and have fewer dissatisfied personnel; or hire more competent "ancillaries" and invite organizational problems.

Considerations of prestige within the organization introduce more complex problems. Since prestige refers to attitudes members have toward each other, it may be only slightly influenced by acts of the administration. Attitudes and their expression, especially the more subtle forms, cannot be legislated by administrative fiat. Furthermore, administrative action may actually have serious disruptive consequences: it may result in coerced co-operation which reduces the reward value of members' behavior for each other, thereby removing an important source for members' motivation. Administrative attempts to co-ordinate activities and clarify roles through formal decrees may reduce the voluntary character of co-operative acts. Since members' attitudes of appreciation and respect are often conveyed through their voluntary co-operation, the coercion of co-operative acts may remove an important source of satisfaction and motivation for organizational personnel.

Still, there may be courses of action open for alleviating prestige problems. Since privileges and salary are associated with prestige, granting "ancillaries" prestige privileges and salary increases may offset the group's dissatisfaction. However, efforts to satisfy the prestige demands of one group of "ancillaries" may be followed by demands from other "ancillaries." Again, the administrator may face a dilemma.

Important in the problem of prestige in mental hospitals is the phenomenon of blocked mobility. The ceiling of one profession is the floor of another. The problem is a serious one. "Ancillaries" can never expect promotion to the top of the organizational hierarchy, or even to the level next above. Although desires and expectations for greater prestige are intimately involved in the drive for professionalization among "ancillaries," such desires and expectations must remain blocked.

A partial solution to this problem is the policy that might be

called "lateral echeloning." [12] According to this policy, arrangements could be made with other agencies—such as near-by uni-
versities—to give appointments to "ancillaries," thereby allowing
them greater professional identity and possible opportunity for
promotion. This has much to commend it. Professionally trained
persons are likely to attain higher levels of satisfaction if they can
pursue their special interests in an environment where they receive the stimulation of their colleagues. However, joint appointments may result in greater identification with one's profession
and the organization where the secondary appointment is held.
The hospital may have too many cosmopolitans whose primary
loyalty is to their profession and too few locals whose loyalties
lie with the local organization.

Along with this mobility block, and a high degree of status
consciousness,[13] in mental hospitals we find an increased emphasis on "democratization" in some therapeutically oriented hospitals. Accompanying the trend of therapeutic attitudes toward
patient care is a democratic and egalitarian ideology and philosophy.[14] The psychiatrists' request for more "equal-status participation" is echoed by "ancillary" requests for more equal-status
recognition.[15] Perhaps the advocates of these changes in hospitals
do not fully realize that prestige ("status") is a scarce com-
modity, that for one to have more prestige means that others
must have less. A community of equals is a fiction, particularly
a community composed of several different groups. Despite their
proclamations to the contrary, it is not likely that psychiatrists
will accept their "ancillaries" as their status equals—at least most
will not. Consequently, it is probably best to dispense with a myth
which "ancillaries" recognize as such. Conflict between myth and

12. William A. Caudill, *The Psychiatric Hospital as a Small Society* (Cambridge: Harvard University Press, 1958), p. 342.
13. See especially Paul Barrabee, "A Study of a Mental Hospital: The Effect
of Its Social Structure on Its Functions," (unpublished Ph.D. dissertation,
Department of Social Relations, Harvard University, 1951).
14. See Greenblatt, York, and Brown, *From Custodial to Therapeutic . . . ,*
pp. 421-22; Doris C. Gilbert and Daniel J. Levinson, " 'Custodialism' and
'Humanism' in Mental Hospital Structure and in Staff Ideology," in Milton
Greenblatt, Daniel J. Levinson, and Richard H. Williams (eds.), *The Patient and the Mental Hospital* (Glencoe: The Free Press, 1957), p. 20; and
Mark Lefton, Simon Dinitz, and Benjamin Pasamanick, "Decision-Making
in a Mental Hospital: Real, Perceived, and Ideal," *American Sociological
Review,* XXIV (1959), 822-29.
15. See L. Kelley, *Training in Clinical Psychology* (New York: Prentice-Hall,
1950), p. 145.

reality, especially when the conflict is recognized, may create unnecessary strain. Although we do not know to what extent this
phenomenon entered into problems described in this book, other
evidence indicates that it may produce dissatisfaction among
"ancillary" personnel.[16]

To say that administrators are relatively helpless to correct
most problems which have their origin in broad social processes
—over which they have little or no control—is not to say that
they should ignore these problems. As we have indicated above,
alternative courses of action are often available. Such action that
is taken, however, should be based on a clear knowledge of the
existing circumstances and probable consequences of different
courses of action. This will require more active administrative
participation than some psychiatrists appear willing to give, and
it will require that action be based on a knowledge of the structure of social relationships rather than personality theory. It will
further require that psychiatrists cease ignoring, or trying to ignore, differences of authority, status, and role, as well as trying
to perceive and relate to hospital personnel as "individuals"
rather than as incumbents of positions in a social structure.
Otherwise, basic organizational and structural elements which are
the source of many hospital social problems will remain ignored.

Many persons argue that among the greatest needs of mental
hospitals are adequate facilities, more money, and competent professional personnel. The present writer's rather unsystematic observations of several state mental hospitals leads him to agree.
There is no doubt that effective psychiatric treatment requires adequate facilities and competent personnel. If this book does nothing else, however, we think it shows that once the problems of
adequate financing and competent personnel have been solved,
other problems appear. For once you gather under the same roof
a number of different professional groups with overlapping skills,
you may invite the problems of competition for prestige and
salary, conflicting conceptions of role duties, desires—and demands—for greater autonomy and independence, and other problems which create conflict among personnel and add problems for
the administrator. Only the naïve believe that once the problems
of economics and personnel have been solved the dedication and
competence of mental health professionals will prevent the occurrence of organizational conflict and tension.

16. Lefton, Dinitz, and Pasamanick, "Decision-Making in a Mental Hospital. . . ."

INDEX

INDEX

Administrator, problems of, 254-59
Admissions Officer, 65
Admissions procedure, on inpatient service, 65-66; changes in, 79-80; psychiatric social workers' attitude toward change in, 80-81; effect of change in, on psychiatric social workers, 80-82
"Ancillary" services, 22
Appreciative standard, 185, 241
Approach-avoidance conflict, 144
Attending man, 22, 24
Attitudes, and overt acts, 9, 154, 158, 192. *See also* Rewards, Expressive orientations, Prestige
Authority, of doctor, 13
Authority structure, medical-"ancillary," 75
Autonomy, "ancillary" professions and, 23-24; of residents, 25, 75; clinical psychologists' desire for, 94-106. *See also* Bureaucracy

Battery testing, 85, 89-90
Battery test referrals, difficulties in, 88
Blocked mobility, 24, 257
Brown, Robert G., 112, 113
Bureaucracy, and clinical psychologists' autonomy, 99-105, 276; and expressive gratification, 153-57; and "ancillary" personnel, 255; and professional autonomy, 255
"Bureaucratization," 249

Casework, in psychiatric social workers' role definition, 64; and psycho-

therapy, 172, 216-17; as dominant social work specialty, 194
Casework referral, on inpatient service, 65-66; as dependent upon residents' judgment, 66; on child psychiatric service, 67
Central patient index, 203
Chief resident, 22, 24, 37; and psychiatric social workers' use of, 69; in *tertius gaudens,* 119
Clinical psychologists, academic background of, 7, 93; role of, 85-86; referral procedure, 86-92; vague referrals to, 90; research, 99-104; role preference, 99, 105; function of joint appointments for, 104-15; and perception of psychiatrists' attitude, 148-52; as comparative reference group for social workers, 163-65; professional self image of, 231
Coalition, 226; attempt to form, 76-78
Compliance, overt, *vs.* internalization, 73-74
Conforming behavior, 98, 106, 123. *See also* J-curve
Conformity with normative order, 17
Consensus, lack of, on organizational goals, 23
Consequences of behavior, as opposed to motive, 43
Coser, Rose Laub, 127
Cosmopolitans among social workers, role definition of, 198; and problem of prestige, 198-200; and integration, 201-8
Cost, defined, 17; of deprivation, 18; anticipation of, 43n; of time and ef-

263

Date Due